From Prototype to Product

This book is for Nick, Ryan, Luke and all the other young and budding engineers out there. Hope this helps you launch hundreds of products over the next 30 years.

From Prototype to Product

A Practical Guide for Electronic Engineers

1st Edition

Seggy T Segaran

An Ohm Books Publication

First published in 2013 by Ohm Books, UK

9, The Pastures
York
YO24 2JE
UK

While the author, publisher and contributors believe that the information and guidance given in this handbook is correct, all parties must rely upon their own skill and judgement when making use of it. Neither the author, the publisher nor any contributor assume any liability to anyone for any loss or damage caused by any error or omission in the work, whether such error or omission is the result of negligence or any other cause. Where reference is made to legislation it is not to be considered as legal advice. Any and all such liability is disclaimed.

ISBN 978-0-9561537-9-1

A CIP catalogue record for this book is available from the British Library.

Cover design by Laura Murray of Peanut Designs.

CONTENTS

INTRODUCTION

Electronic product development is a specialist field. It requires not only a good understanding of the technology - it demands a thorough knowledge of the whole process of taking an electronic design through the various stages and making it available for sale.

This includes the design of the enclosure, making sure that the product can be manufactured economically and that component tolerances have been taken into account. A good product designer also has to take into account regulatory requirements such as emissions and safety, make sure that the product is documented accurately for production and be confident that it can be easily supported in the field.

Universities and colleges are very good at giving their students a solid grounding in the technology such as circuit design and analysis, embedded software and using the latest design tools. Graduates are very capable of producing prototype designs that work. What they learn when they start in industry is how to turn those prototypes into commercial products that sell at a price that generates a profit for their companies.

In other professions like medicine, accountancy and law, this gap is filled formally during the training phase. Practitioners have to work in a hospital, in an accountancy or law firm before they can qualify and start to practice. However in engineering, this is not normally part of the requirements. Graduates often are put to work designing products without any grounding in the many aspects of product design that will help them to produce winning products.

What I have attempted to do in this book is to try and prepare the new graduate for the world of engineering. Throughout the book I have taken examples from products that I have worked on. In over 35 years in engineering I have been fortunate to be involved in the design and launch of more than 30 different products. I have also worked on a number of other products as a consultant. Many were successful but some did not quite live up to expectations. I am keen to pass on the lessons learnt from all these experiences to a new generation of engineers.

Seggy T Segaran

Summer 2013

DESIGN ISSUES

This section covers a number of topics that will be useful to the electronic engineer. They are all based on my experience of designing numerous analogue products with embedded software.

Power Supplies

Rechargeable Batteries

Tolerance

Embedded Software

Testing

Power Supplies

During the course of their degree most electronic engineers take the power supply as a given. Concentrating mainly on their own electronic designs, they tend to use bench top supplies to power their circuits. When taking a design from the prototype stage to getting it ready as a commercial product, designing the power supply is a critical design process. Many projects have fallen by the wayside due to too little attention being paid to what most engineers think of as a trivial task. In this chapter we will look at power supply design using a few case studies.

Linear Power Supplies
Case study: Piper Lifeline

I was involved with this project during my time at Tunstall Telecom. This was an alarm telephone for the elderly with a radio trigger. When alerted, it would dial a control centre and after a handshake would transmit a sequence of digits to identify the caller. The receptionist at the control centre could use this to alert a mobile warden to assist the caller.

The unit was powered from the mains, using a linear power supply. During the design of this I made a mistake that resulted in a number of these telephones not performing in the field.

There are many books and guides to good linear power supply design. I made sure that the transformer supplied when used in a circuit with a diode bridge rectifier, smoothing capacitor and regulator, gave 12V DC when loaded at 0.5A. This was what we had worked out as the required performance from the power supply. It was fairly straightforward to make sure that the regulator had enough head room and had the right sized heat sink for the expected heat dissipation. The smoothing capacitor was sized appropriately to keep the ripple to a few millivolts.

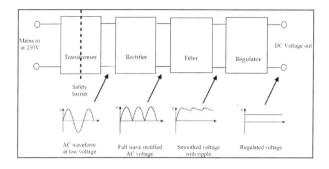

Block diagram of linear power supply

The mistake I made was not to allow for variation in mains voltage. I had worked out all the above calculations for a voltage of around 230 to 240V. The first field trial units were placed in remote Lincolnshire and started misbehaving. Detailed investigation highlighted the fact that the mains voltage was down to around 210 to 220V at these sites. The resulting ripple in the supply rails affected the performance of the signalling circuits resulting in the telephones not being able to complete the handshake.

Variac

In practice, the mains voltage in the UK can vary from 190V up to 250V. This makes the design of linear power supplies quite a tricky task. There is a risk of the power supply not delivering enough voltage and having too much ripple at the lower end of this range. If the voltage were to be at the higher end, then there is a risk of too much heat dissipation which can be a fire risk.

The best tool to test the performance of a linear power supply is a Variac. This allows the mains voltage to be varied over the desired range. No good design lab should be without one.

Switching Power Supplies
Case study: Testel Telephone Exchange Simulator

The Testel was one of the telecom test instruments that we designed and manufactured at Tele-Products back in 1992. The unit had to generate a number of power rails at 12V, 5V and 48V. We also wanted it to be battery powered for field use. We chose to use a 12V sealed lead acid battery as this had the required capacity.

After considering various options we settled on a linear power supply to provide the 12V. The 5V was produced from this using a linear 5V regulator. Both the 12V and 5V regulators used hefty heat sinks. The 48V was produced using a switching regulator from the 12V. The circuit for this is shown below.

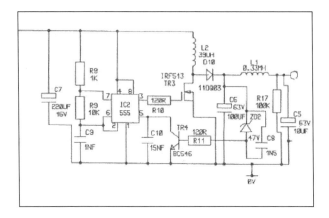

Diagram of a 12V to 48V switching circuit

The free running 555 timer switches the mosfet transistor

(TR3) on and off. When the current through the inductor is switched off, the voltage rises to above 48V, due the back EMF. At this point, the 555 drive is turned off due to the 48V zener diode (ZD2) conducting and switching the transistor (TR4) on. When the load on the 48V rail is high, the 555 is on for longer. This regulates the output voltage to 48V.

This way the 12V battery could provide all 3 power rails and keep the Testel powered for more than 1 hour of use. The disadvantage of the 12V to 48V switching circuit is that it does produce a fair bit of circuit noise.

The Testel is an example of the use of a linear and switching power supplies to allow the unit to work from a 12V battery. The type of design used here is referred to as a DC to DC converter as it steps up the 12V to 48V.

Switching versus Linear supplies

Switching power supplies work by 'chopping' the mains voltage and then using a high frequency transformer to step down the voltage. The transistor that does the 'chopping' is controlled through a feedback loop and is only kept on for as long as is required. This way, only the amount of current required by the circuit is taken from the mains.

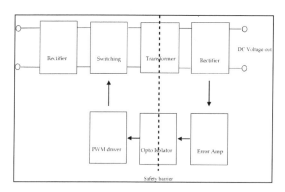

Block diagram of a switching supply

Switching power supplies have a number of benefits over

linear power supplies. They are more efficient as they only draw as much power as is required and because of this there is less heat dissipated in the components. They can work over a wider range of input voltages, typically 90V to 250V rms so that the same circuit can be used around the world irrespective of whether the mains supply is 230V or 110V. Finally, as the switching is at a much higher frequency the transformer can be much smaller resulting in a compact unit.

Switching PSU (12V/500mA) and linear PSU (12V/300mA)

Switching power supplies generate a lot of circuit noise both at the output and at the input. They need careful PCB layout and screening to minimise this noise. This is necessary to prevent it from affecting circuit performance and meet the emission requirements for the product.

Innovative power supply design
Case study: Meteor

During the design phase of a project careful consideration of power requirements can often result in an elegant and innovative solution. This happened during the design of the Meteor which was a Caller ID device for a PC. This product originally was intended to have three connections. One was to the PC serial port, another to the telephone line and lastly an external plug-top power supply. The circuit needed 5V to operate and - 10V for the RS232 signals.

When designing the RS232 interface we realised that this was capable of supplying 10V with a current capability of a few milliamps. Luckily we only needed the unit to work when the PC was switched on. Close investigation also showed that we could derive the - 10V from the RS232 port of the PC itself.

A detailed power budget analysis resulted in the whole Meteor circuit being powered from the serial RS232 port of the PC. We even had spare current to drive a couple of LEDs.

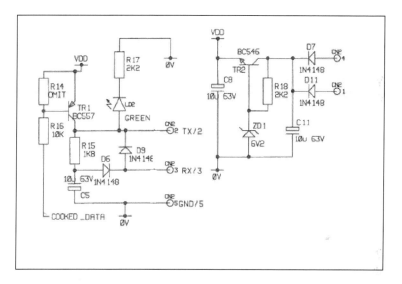

Circuit of the Meteor power supply & RS232 interface

Diodes D7 and D11 supply +10V to the simple 5V regulator design, consisting of transistor (TR2) and the 6V2 zener.

The PC keeps the Rx line at -10V. A capacitor (C5) is charged to this voltage through a diode (D6). When the transistor (TR1) is switched off, the voltage at the Tx line is -10V and when it is switched on it is at +5V.

This resulted in a compact low cost unit which was easy to connect up. All the user had to do was to connect a lead to the telephone line and another to the serial port of the PC.

Battery life
Case study: MemoryPAT

Here is an example of product cost running out of control if enough attention is not paid to current consumption during the design phase. The MemoryPAT was quite a recent project that was designed by an external team. This is a battery powered Portable Appliance Tester incorporating a display. During the design phase, a rechargeable NiMH PP3 battery was proposed to provide more than 500 tests between charges. The most common battery of this type has a capacity of around 200 mAh. The budget per test works out as 0.4 mAh.

On the final design, the capacity per test worked out at more than twice the budget at nearly 1 mAh. The interim solution to this problem was to use a battery pack made up of 7 cells with a capacity of 600 mAh. This gave the required battery life but cost 3 times as much as the battery originally proposed.

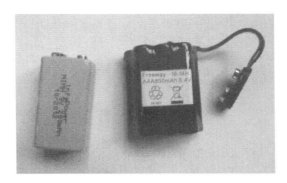

NiMH: PP3 battery and a 7 x AAA battery pack

How could this project have been managed better? The power consumption per test depended on the way the tester generated the various voltages and how long the test took. The design used a PWM circuit to generate most of the required voltages. While this was a very flexible approach the time taken to generate the voltage was longer as it took a few seconds for this circuit to reach the required voltage. What was required was an iterative approach where every design decision was subject to a power analysis.

Summary

Any engineer involved in electronic product design has to pay careful attention to the power supply design. A poorly designed power supply can result in a product not performing or worse still bursting into flames during use. Careful attention to power consumption can result in elegant designs that are easy to use. If not enough attention is paid to this, the product costs can spiral as a result of solving issues to do with higher than expected power consumption.

Rechargeable Batteries

Many electronic products make use of batteries. A good engineer has to have an understanding of the various battery types that are available and which one to choose for different applications. Battery performance can be adversely affected by the different charging technologies used so it's important to take this into account during the design.

Rechargeable batteries are used in different ways in products. Some products use mains for normal operation and the battery is only used occasionally for emergency backup, such as in an alarm or Uninterruptible Power Supply (UPS). In others the battery is charged and then powers the unit, such as in mobile telephones. Batteries are also used to start cars where they have to supply a very high current for a short period. The choice of the type of battery and their charging depends on the application they are used in.

Lead Acid Battery
Case study: Testel Exchange Simulator

This product used a sealed Lead Acid battery to allow it to be used without a mains supply. This type of battery was chosen because of its large capacity of 1.2 Ah.

Sealed Lead-Acid battery

With the circuit taking around 400mA during operation, this battery was able to provide a couple of hours of operation. The application was more transportable than portable and the size and weight of the battery was not an issue.

The Testel was mostly used with a mains power supply. The conventional way to charge a Lead Acid battery over a long period is by the float charge method. A voltage of 13.7V is applied to the battery permanently to maintain its charge. It's important to regulate this voltage as too high or too low a voltage can result in reduced battery life.

Discharging a battery completely can also lead to reduced capacity. With the Testel we did not incorporate a circuit to prevent discharge below a certain voltage. However we did provide a battery low indicator to remind the user to switch the unit off or connect it to the mains.

Solar Charge Controllers

Lead-Acid batteries are used widely to store energy in solar and wind power systems when they are used off-grid. Solar Charge Controllers incorporate charge and discharge control circuitry for use in these applications.

Solar Charge Controller

They prevent overcharging of the battery by either switching off the charge voltage or regulating it to the correct level. They also have circuitry which disconnects the battery if its voltage drops too low. This prevents damage to the battery caused by it discharging completely.

Nickel Cadmium (Ni-Cd) Battery
Case study: Piper Lifeline

The Piper Lifeline used a Ni-Cd battery pack to enable the unit to make emergency calls in the absence of mains power. As this was a standby application, the battery pack was trickle charged to keep it topped up and ready for use, in the event of a mains failure.

The recommended trickle charge rate for this type of battery is C/10 to C/20, where C is the capacity of the battery. A constant current source is the best way to ensure that a set amount of current is used for this charging.

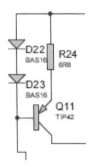

Constant current source set to about 100 mA

The two diodes bias the base of the transistor (Q11) to around 1.2V below the supply. If you allow for the emitter base drop, this results in a voltage of around 0.6V across R24, irrespective of supply voltage. This sets the current source to around 100mA to charge the battery.

Most mains failures are of short duration and the battery pack was able to power the unit for more than 2 hours for this purpose. The product also incorporated a 'mains fail' alarm. The persistent beep from the Piper Lifeline alerted the user to any accidental mains failure such as the unit being unplugged. This alarm plus the use of a simple rechargeable battery pack gave the user peace of mind that the unit would still be able to summon help if it was needed.

Nickel Metal Hydride (Ni-MH) Battery
Case study: BattPAT Portable Appliance Tester

This tester is designed to be powered from the battery all the time and this is charged as required. As this was a much later design than the Piper Lifeline, a Ni-MH Battery pack was used. A 9V, PP3 battery pack was used consisting of 7 NiMH cells in series with a capacity of 200mAh.

BattPAT PCB assembly showing the Ni-MH PP3 battery

In this type of application, it is important to charge the battery as quickly as possible without damaging the cells. Fast charging is possible but to avoid the risk of overcharging, the charge circuit has to detect when the battery is fully charged. In theory, this can be done by detecting the drop in voltage when it is fully charged. However this is quite small and can lead to premature cessation of charging.

To charge the battery quickly we adopted a two stage approach. A constant current circuit with the current set to C/2 was used to charge the battery for an hour. This quickly brought the battery capacity up to 50%. Then a trickle charge of C/40 was used to top up the battery. This meant that after an hour of charging the BattPAT was ready for use. However if it was left charging overnight, there was no risk as it simply continued to trickle charge with no danger of overcharging.

When a battery pack is being charged and discharged continuously, it is important not to discharge the battery completely. If this happens there is a risk that one cell in the pack could get reverse charged and be damaged. This is due to the fact that the cells all have slightly different capacity and discharge at different rates.

Ni-MH cells are typically 1.4V when fully charged and deliver 1.25V when providing a current of up to 0.5 Amps. A voltage monitor was used to check the battery voltage in operation. If this dropped below around 8V (1.15V per cell) then the BattPAT will not carry on with the test. This ensured that the unit was put on charge well before the battery pack discharged completely.

One should also take into account that in order to charge a Ni-MH battery to its full capacity one needs to 'overcharge' it. That is the battery has to be charged to around 130 to 140 % capacity to be charged fully. This is due to self discharge. Ni-MH batteries can lose up to 20 to 30 % of their charge on the first day and continue to lose between 1 to 4 % every day.

Detecting battery charge state

In many applications it is useful to know the exact charge state of a battery. For example, if we knew that the pack still had 50% of its capacity left, then we would only need to top it up by another 50% or so. However this is easier said than done as the battery voltage is fairly constant during discharge and cannot be used to indicate the charge state.

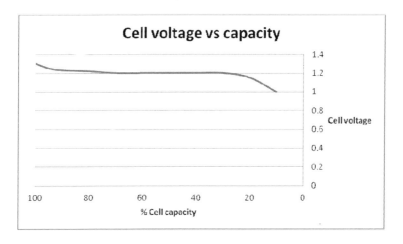

Ni-MH cell voltage vs. capacity

In some applications, like in mobile phones, more sophisticated techniques are used to keep track of battery charge state. This is usually done by measuring the current drawn from the battery and using this information to calculate how much capacity is left in the battery. It is important to reset the charge state to 100% when the battery is charged to maintain accuracy.

Rechargeable Lithium cell
Case study: Meter Logger

This product detects pulses from an electricity meter or other utility meter and logs this to memory. A Real Time Clock chip was used to make sure that the data was logged in the correct time slot. A battery was used to enable the Real Time Clock to keep time in the absence of mains power. Due to the compact size of the product and the low capacity required from the battery, a Lithium Manganese Dioxide cell was the natural choice.

Meter Logger with the Lithium cell

The other benefit of using this type of Lithium cell is that it can be trickle charged by using a constant voltage equal to the maximum voltage of the battery. This results in a very simple charging circuit. As the Meter Logger only used a single cell, a voltage of 3.7V was used for this and a resistor of 560 ohm was used to limit the current.

Lithium cells can burst into flames if overcharged and deep discharge can short circuit the cells. For these reasons it pays to take extreme care in the handling and the use of these devices.

Note: If you are planning to use Li-ion cells then please note these cannot be trickle charged and require complex charging circuits to prevent them being damaged.

Summary

The choice of the type of battery and method of charging depends on the product and the way that it is being used. A good design engineer needs to be aware of the range of options available to him and the benefits of using a particular battery technology.

Tolerance

Many electronics design courses concentrate on digital electronics and embedded software and pay little attention to basic analogue electronics. However it is essential to have a good understanding of analogue circuits to interface micro-controllers to the 'real world'.

This chapter is not intended to be a crash course in this field as it is covered by many excellent books. However one area of analogue electronics that graduate engineers have to grasp well is an understanding of component tolerances and how this will affect the performance of a product.

Transistor gain
Case study: Viscount Telephone

In this design we used a NPN transistor as a switch. When using a bipolar transistor such as this as a switch, it is important to make sure that there is sufficient base current to saturate the transistor. For example when the switched collector current is expected to be around 100mA, then if the gain of the transistor is x200, a base current of 1mA or more is required to saturate this transistor. That is the base current times gain has to be much greater than the collector current.

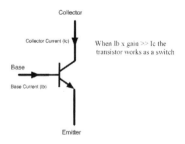

NPN transistor working as a switch

However, the gain of a bipolar transistor can vary enormously in production. The data sheet for one manufacturer of the NPN states the gain as varying from 100 to 300. For the purpose of this design, we have to work with the lowest gain of 100 and make sure that the base current is 2mA or more to ensure that the transistor is saturated.

Analogue to Digital Conversion
Case study: BattPAT Portable Appliance Tester

In this design, the reference voltage for the A to D convertor was the supply voltage which was provided by a 5V regulator with a 5% tolerance. At first sight, this would imply that there would be a 5% tolerance on all the A to D conversions. The conventional way to resolve this would be to use an external reference that was a much better tolerance, for example an LT1009 which is a 2.5V reference with a tolerance of 0.2%.

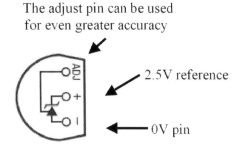

The adjust pin can be used
for even greater accuracy

2.5V reference

0V pin

LT1009 voltage reference

However, the final values that were required were the ratio of 2 measurements. This had the effect of cancelling any inaccuracies in the A to D and giving a highly accurate reading.

For example, say we were measuring 2 voltages of 1V and 2V. At the worst case tolerance, we will have a reading of 1.05 and 2.1 for the 2 voltages (5% high). However when we divide 2.1 by 1.05 we still get 2, which is the same when we divide 2 by 1 thus cancelling the inaccuracy of the A to D conversion.

Potentiometers
Case study: Relate 1000 Caller ID Telephone

I was involved in this product around 1995 working as a technical consultant to a supplier to British Telecom. This was the first Caller ID telephone in the UK market working to the BT specification.

Relate 1000 Caller ID telephone

There will be occasions where component tolerance cannot be designed out and the designer will use a potentiometer to be adjusted during production testing. In the Relate 1000 telephone, we used a phase locked loop with a potentiometer to detect a 2130Hz signal prior to receipt of the Caller ID data from the exchange. In theory this could have been done by the microcontroller. However we could not achieve the required sensitivity with a digital solution.

When using potentiometers in a design the design engineer has to make sure that they are set up correctly during production. Due to a basic error, there were many pre-production Relate 1000 units that failed to operate correctly in the field.

Adjustment pot inside Relate 1000

The original production set up used a 2130Hz generator, and the potentiometer was adjusted until this frequency was detected. The production operative then glued the pot in this position. What we had could be shown graphically as follows.

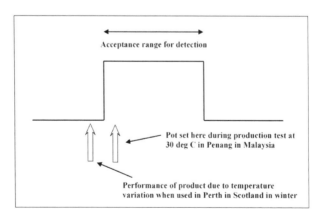

Original detector set up during production

These pre-production units were manufactured in Penang in Malaysia and shipped over to the UK for field trials which took place in January. The temperature difference and the poor set up resulted in many field trial units failing to detect the 2130Hz tone.

The set up procedure was improved as follows. The potentiometer was adjusted until the 2130Hz was detected. The pot was continued to be rotated until the 2130Hz was not detected anymore. Then the pot was backed up until it was half way between the 2 detection extremes. Then it was glued in place. What this new set up achieved could be shown graphically as follows.

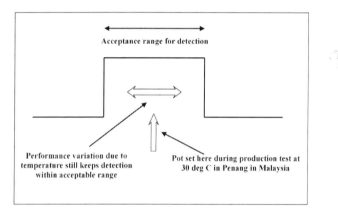

Improved detector set up during production

Variation with temperature
Case study: Return Loss Tester

This was the first test instrument manufactured by Tele-Products. It used precision components and was used by design engineers to measure the Return loss to various impedances used by telecom products around the world.

Not only did we use high precision components in this instrument, we also chose components with a low variation with temperature. Most resistors and capacitors values do change with temperature. When capacitors are used for decoupling their accuracy is not too important. However when they are used in filters and where measurement accuracy is important, this temperature variation can be a critical factor.

Polystyrene capacitor

The Polystyrene capacitors that we used in the Return Loss tester were supplied in a 1% tolerance band, had a low temperature variation of around 200ppm/deg C and good stability with time. For example, a 100nF Polystyrene capacitor's value will vary by 0.4nF over a 10 degrees change in temperature. This represented less than 0.5% change in the value over this temperature range. The long term stability of this capacitor was better than 0.5%.

Summary

Most tolerance problems may not appear during the prototype or pre production stages. Often these are small batches and the chances are that the devices used do not exhibit the variation that is likely to be seen when products are manufactured in large volumes. A good engineer should spend some time trawling through the circuit to identify any potential tolerance issues and fix these before the product is released for manufacture.

Embedded Software

Most Electronic Engineering degrees include a substantial element of embedded programming as this is an important part of an engineer's toolbox. There is an incredible array of microcontroller devices, programming languages and development tools available to today's electronic engineer. The examples below are all from my experiences of working alongside programmers on products and tackling problems during product development.

Switch bounce

I have been involved in many products where a poor understanding of switch bounce has led to a design that had problems in the field. To learn how to deal with this the engineer has to understand exactly what switch bounce is.

When a switch is pressed down, it does not go cleanly from an open state to a closed state. The mechanical components that carry out the switching usually has a settling time, which can vary from a few milliseconds up to almost 30 or 40 milliseconds in some cases. Below is a diagram of the waveform that can be seen when a switch is pressed.

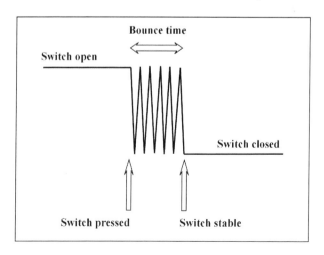

Switch bounce

With microcontrollers running at faster and faster speeds, this switch will be read as being pressed many times, if switch bounce is not catered for. If the switch is used to toggle a parameter on and off on the product, then the microcontroller will detect this many times for just one key press.

If the switch normally has a pull up resistor and is used to take an input low when pressed, then the way to deal with bounce is as follows, for a switch that has a maximum bounce period of say 35 milli seconds.

If this input goes from high to low, then wait 40 milliseconds and check if input is still low. If yes, then switch is pressed and all bounce has finished so set switch pressed flag.

Remember that there will be bounce when the switch is released. So a similar procedure has to be followed to check for this. If this input goes from low to high, then wait 40 milliseconds and check if input is still high. If yes, then switch has been released.

Relay Bounce
Case study: Meter Logger

The meter logger counts pulses from utility meters, using a relay output from the meter. On the early beta versions of this product we found that the counting algorithm was not behaving as expected. This was due to the fact that there was no account of relay bounce at all in the firmware. Once we put in a de-bounce delay of 10 milliseconds for relay closing and opening, everything worked as expected.

Reset Circuit

Microcontrollers depend on a good hardware reset circuit to initialise and start running. Reset circuits should operate once the supply to the microcontroller has reached its working voltage range. Managing the operation of the micro when its supply drops below its operating range, is very important. If output pins are left in an indeterminate state it can lead to unforeseen consequences.

For example, some microcontroller reset circuits are based on a resistor and capacitor in series as shown below. The capacitor ensures that reset input changes only after the supply to the microcontroller has reached a satisfactory level. However, if the supply subsequently drops below this level, this reset circuit will not operate.

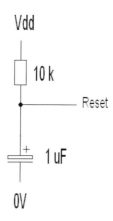

Typical reset circuit

The best way to see if a design is robust enough to withstand power supply variations is by testing. The design engineer should force the supply voltage to various levels and observe the behaviour of the product. Any problems that crop up can then be tackled by implementing firmware of hardware fixes.

**Reset Circuit
Case study: Viscount Telephone**

This product used an early 4-bit microcontroller to manage some of the telephony functions, such as storing telephone numbers and dialling. This circuit was powered from the telephone line. When the telephone was on-hook, there was no current available to power the micro and it was in a shut down state. When the handset was picked up, the supply to the micro was established.

To make sure that the microcontroller started up properly every time, the reset circuit was tied to the off-hook operation. In the unlikely event that the micro was stuck in an indeterminate state, there would be no response from the phone and the likely response of the user would be to flash the hook switch. This would immediately reset the micro and restart operation.

Power Management

When a microcontroller is guaranteed a stable 5V supply with plenty of current available, the design engineer can get their head down and get on with programming. However in many instances, the supply is not always guaranteed and can vary with time. Often there is a need to extend battery life by making sure that power consumption is kept to a minimum.

Battery voltage
Case study: BattPAT Portable Appliance Tester

This tester was powered from a 9V rechargeable battery. It had a battery low indication that was triggered when the battery voltage dropped to around 8.2V. The original design had a second trigger when the battery low voltage reached 7.6V below which it did not operate. However, this check was only carried out when the test was started.

The result was that when the supply voltage dropped below the microcontroller's operating voltage during the test, the unit locked up, not allowing the user to carry on with the testing. The unit was only usable once the battery discharged completely and subsequently charged.

The revised firmware checked for the battery voltage reaching 7.6 during the test as well at the start. If the voltage was too low for normal operation, then the unit indicated this to the user and shut down in an organised fashion. The user then had to put the unit on charge before using it again.

Watchdog timer

Even the best designed software can lock up due to unforeseen circumstances. A particular set of events can keep the software in some sort of endless loop and the only way to recover would be to turn the power off and on. On battery powered systems, this might involve taking the batteries out.

A hardware watchdog timer is a way of the software recovering automatically from these potential lock ups and most microcontrollers have one built in.

In order to use this properly, the designer has to work out the longest time the micro is away doing tasks and then set the watchdog timer to above this period. Then, in the main loop the watchdog timer would need to be retriggered on every pass. If the software were to be locked up in an endless loop somewhere, then the watchdog timer would expire and reset the micro automatically.

Summary

Embedded software is a feature of most electronic products. Managing the power to the microcontrollers and ensuring that they reset properly is an important consideration in any design. Interfacing to the real world such as switches and relays can bring interesting timing issues which have to be managed carefully by the engineer intending to launch robust designs.

Hints and tips regarding embedded software
Geoffrey Swales
Managing Director, Biodigital Ltd

"Learn from your mistakes. The man who never made mistakes, never made anything!"

Button de-bounce

Although de-bounce on button inputs can be implemented in firmware this often leaves the microcontroller exposed to a direct electrical input. Using a small RC filter will reduce bounce from the button and (more importantly) add some impedance into the path from the button to the microcontroller.

I have had issues with products where mains hum picked-up by the mains earth line found its' way onto the metal enclosure of a product (the metal case was correctly connected to the mains earth). This mains hum then passed onto the membrane keypad stuck on the front of the product via capacitive coupling. This mains hum looked like the buttons were being pressed 50 times a second, so the firmware de-bounce was working overtime and the code execution grinded to a halt.

A simply RC filter on each of the button inputs solved the problem.

Firmware basics

Always comment code. It is common practice for software engineers to work on several projects each year and you may have to re-visit code several years after the event (to fix a bug or add enhancements). If your code is not well commented it can make your life much harder in the long run.

Each file (.h, .c, etc) should have a good, clear header text; clearly stating date author, function, etc. See example below.

```
//****************************************************
//***    FILENAME:     BD123-01.C            ***
//***    DATE:         13/06/13              ***
//***    AUTHOR:       GEOFFREY SWALES       ***
//***    COMPANY:      BIODIGITAL LIMITED    ***
//***    CLIENT:       CUSTOMER  LTD         ***
//***    DESCRIPTION:NETWORKED SOMETHING     ***
//***    VERSION:      V0.1                  ***
//****************************************************
//***    VERSION CONTROL:                    ***
//***    V0.1:   INITIAL DEVELOPMENT SYSTEM  ***
//***                                        ***
//****************************************************
```

Each function should also carry a header text stating the purpose, what to pass it and what it returns and any important notes (such as; must be called every 100ms, etc).

Try to keep functions related to a specific piece of hardware (or peripheral) together in the same file. This will help you to build up useful library routines, make it easier to modify the firmware to accommodate new hardware and make it easier to track hardware specific bugs.

Firmware best practice when writing in C

Curly Brackets

ALWAYS use curly brackets after statements, even if they only encase one statement; it is all too easy to put a semi-colon in by mistake with disastrous results:-

```
If(train_in_station)        //only if the train is in the station...
    Open_doors();           // open the doors
```

Can easily be written as (with disastrous consequences):-

```
If(train_in_station);       //only if the train is in the station...do
                            nothing
    Open_doors();           // now open the doors, regardless
```

So always write:-

```
If(train_in_station)          //only is the train is in the station…
{
        Open_doors();         // open the doors
}
```

It won't stop you making mistakes, but the code is less crammed and easier to read, so hopefully you will spot the mistake before people fall out of your speeding train.

Global Variables

Minimise your use of global variables. This is easier said than done when coding for small 8-bit embedded systems with limited resources and certainly no dynamic memory allocation.

Most compilers will work with local variables, re-using their space, where possible. This will yield a more efficient use of the available memory. Global variables lead to opportunistic use in multiple routines, so if one routine modifies a global variable it can have unseen effects on other routines that also use that variable.

Passing variables as arguments to called functions is better as you can easily see what routine is using the variable and how it passes from one function to another. Global variables can be very powerful as a global means of influencing your code, but by minimising their use you will get the best of both worlds.

Pointers

C programmers love pointers as they open the door to more powerful and efficient code, but as they say in all Super Hero films; "this power comes at a cost".

Just one small mistake in handling pointers can lead to data being stored in the wrong location. This can corrupt variables and lead to erratic function behavior in remote parts of the code, miles away from the actual problem.

The general rule is to only use pointers when nothing else will suffice. When accessing strings; use indexes. When accessing bytes of large variables use bit shifts.

Bugs

No matter how good you are at programming, as your code gets bigger you will encounter bugs. Worse still your customers will encounter bugs. No matter how much you test the code, there is always a chance that there is a bug lurking somewhere.

Bugs are very easy to fix, the problem is finding out what causes them. Some bugs will occur if a certain sequence of events occurs. Re-creating this sequence and witnessing the bug is quite straight forward. Debugging will allow you to see what is occurring in the code and thus solve the situation.

Unfortunately some bugs are more elusive and the worst are the random bugs! These can easily make it into products as they may only manifest themselves after hours of operation (or even months!). Because some systems may demonstrate the bugs almost immediately while others may run fine for months, it is very easy to pass the bug off as a hardware issue.

Random bugs are nearly always a result of code crashes between an interrupt routine and a certain part of the main code. Because the bug will only occur if the interrupt code is executed at the precise time the certain mains code is also executing it is like an aligning of the planets and as such occurs very rarely and randomly.

The trick to resolving this is to see what registers, library functions or even similar code operations are common to both the interrupt routines and the main code. Then slowly remove commands from the interrupt and place them in the main code (this may not be as efficient but it is just temporary) until the code becomes stable long-term. Once the problem code is found you then have to devise a work around.

Geoffrey Swales is Managing Director of Biodigital Ltd, a company he founded in 2002. Biodigital have designed hundreds of products for clients over the years and now have embarked on developing their own products for spin-off companies.

www.biodigital.co.uk

Testing

Testing is an integral part of the design process. An experienced engineer will ensure a design is robust by testing fully to prove the performance of the product. He will also have a big input into the key stages such as production and throughout the life of the product such as repair and maintenance.

Time and again, many products have failed to perform in the field due to the lack of a proper test regime during the design proving phase. It is important to properly exercise the product by subjecting it to the range of conditions that can be expected in the field.

Many engineers carry out functional tests but fail to carry out tests at 'worst case' conditions. In my career as an electronics engineer I have had many conversations with other engineers that have gone a bit like this.

Engineer: "The telephone is working in my office but not when I take it to the customer's site".

Me: "OK. What range of signal levels did you use for your design test?"

Engineer: "Oh. Well I just used my telephone line in the office to check that it was working".

Design Tests
Case study: Testel Telephone Exchange Simulator

What we attempted to do with the Testel was to provide the design engineer with a bench test instrument that could be adjusted to represent the 'worst case' conditions that could be experienced in the field. For example, a typical telephone line could be anything up to 7 km from the nearest exchange. This will have an effect on the telephone line current as well as the signal level. The Testel had a switch to set the line current and another one to represent line attenuation.

Testel 200 front panel

If used properly, the Testel can fully exercise any line connected telecoms unit and ensure that it performs properly in the field.

Case study: Meteor Caller ID unit

This unit has been selling successfully for more than 10 years. One of the reasons for its success is its reliability in the field. Many competing units have failed to achieve the same performance.

The level of the Caller ID signal can vary widely from one telephone line to another. The worst case signal can be as low as -40dBV. This is around a few millivolts. We made sure that the Meteor could perform at this level during the design testing. Every production unit is also tested to ensure it can detect signals at this low level ensuring its continued success.

Case study: BattPAT Portable Appliance Tester

This battery powered tester operates off a 9V rechargeable NiMH battery. The voltage of this battery varies from 9.6V when fully charged down to 8V when the unit stops working. We had to ascertain the accuracy of the test results over this range of voltages.

During the design verification stage, we identified a number of problems with the measurement accuracy over this voltage range, which were subsequently fixed by the designer.

Design Verification Testing

Although the design engineer needs to be involved in determining this test sequence it is quite important that another engineer actually carry out these tests. In my experience, the design engineer is too close to the product to do this testing objectively.

Often the test instrumentation for this type of detailed testing may not be readily available and may need to be 'cobbled together' temporarily to allow testing to be carried out.

Production testing - manual
Case study: BattPAT Portable Appliance Tester

This tester displayed a PASS or a FAIL using green and red LEDs on the front panel. As there were no test results displayed on the tester we had to come with an appropriate test for this product. As the BattPAT was made in relatively low volumes there was not much benefit in investing in automated test equipment. We decided on a final functional test to verify its performance.

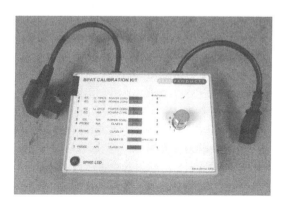

Test kit for BattPAT

The production test kit for the BattPAT consisted of 'just pass' and 'just fail' components in a test box that plugged into the BattPAT like an appliance under test. For example, the pass limit for the Earth Continuity test was less than 250 milliohm. The test box had a 225 milliohm resistor for the 'just pass' and a 275 milliohm for the 'just fail'. These were used to ensure that the BattPAT met its published specification for Earth Continuity. A similar approach was adopted for the other measurements.

Production testing - automatic
Case study: Viscount Telephone

As this product was manufactured in such high volumes a 2-stage test was used. A 'bed-of-nails' test fixture was used to test the components and some of the circuits.

Bed-of-nails test fixture

This was followed by a functional test on the finished product. At this stage the keypad, hook switch, handset, and ringer were tested functionally.

Note: It is important to avoid the tendency to over test at the production stage. The objective is to determine that the design has been manufactured correctly - i.e. the right components have been inserted (or placed) and soldered correctly. The production test is NOT intended to be a design verification test.

Repair of production failures

Most production failures are likely be due to manufacturing faults like wrong components, correct components inserted wrongly or soldering faults. However some may be due to design faults. It is important to get involved in the analysis of production faults to determine if any are due to tolerance issues and use this information to improve the design.

Repair of field returns

Many companies are organised so that once a product is launched the design engineer goes onto another project and does not get involved in field returns. Sometimes an external organisation is used to design a product with no involvement in assisting with any faulty units. It is not unusual for me to hear statements like those below from design engineers:

"Once it leaves here we are not going to see it again so does it matter if the battery is glued down and cannot be taken off?"

"We are not going to have any failures on this product so there is no point in thinking about repairs".

Failures in the field are a fact of life, even on the best designed product. An experienced engineer will make sure that the design can be tested easily by repair technicians (this might require special test modes to be designed into the product). They will also specify a repair test and help build test equipment for this purpose.

Getting involved in the repair of field returns will allow the engineer to perform a Pareto (see appendix) analysis and improve the reliability of the product.

Summary

Testing is an integral part of the design process. The design verification has to be done forensically and is best carried out by someone other than the designer. The production test is to check that the design has been manufactured as planned. A good engineer will get involved in the testing of production failures and field returns and use the information from this to improve the design.

DESIGN FOR MANUFACTURE

Taking a product from the working prototype stage and turning it into one that can be manufactured and made available for sale is a skill that comes with many years of experience. Here are a couple of key areas that need close attention.

Enclosures

PCB Technology

Enclosures

Many university designed projects stop at the board assembly level. This means that the graduate when he enters the world of engineering is not quite in a position to take an informed decision on what type of enclosure to use for his products. However, the first thing that the customer sees is the finished product and many form an opinion on the product based on the enclosure.

The choice of the right enclosure is also important to the final manufacturing cost of the product. Some enclosures can end up in doubling the cost of materials and erode margins. This chapter looks at a number of product enclosure options.

Injection Moulding
Case study: Viscount Telephone

Viscount telephone made for British Telecom

This was one of my earliest projects when I started work at Standard Telephones and Cables (STC) at New Southgate in London. I was part of the team that designed the electronics for this product. There was a dedicated industrial design team that worked on the enclosure. There was good communication between the teams and this gave me an opportunity to see the design process at work.

When STC won the contract from BT, the expected orders were around 500,000 units per annum. The enclosure was going to be injection moulded. Although the tooling costs would be high, the actual enclosure parts could be moulded for a few pence. Design and tooling costs of around £250,000 would be amortised over the expected 4 year life of the product into 12.5p per unit. (Amortising is a way of theoretically spreading the upfront design costs over the life of a product. It is a useful exercise to see if the design costs can be justified).

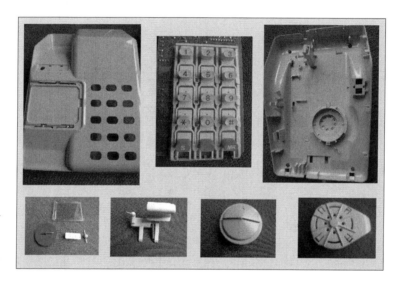

Individual moulded parts from the Viscount telephone

With such a high throughput, it was also important to keep manufacturing times as low as possible. The PCB assembly simply clips into the base and the whole product is held together by using just one screw.

Tooling for Injection mouldings

Tooling costs for injection moulding can vary from £5k to £50k depending on the complexity of the tool, the number of cavities and whether it is hardened for high quantities or a soft tool for small production runs. The design of the tool is a specialist skill. Electronic engineers that want to go down this route will need to contract an industrial designer to work with. A capable designer will be able to present a number of design options, liaise with tool designers and injection moulding companies to produce the enclosures.

Injection moulding tool

In my experience most industrial designers will be able to get quotes from the Far East as well. Often this is just for the tool, with the actual injection moulding taking place in the UK.

However if the moulding is to take place in the Far East, then take care to factor in additional time for communications and quality control. Tackling defective parts when you have paid and taken delivery of them can be a problem. There are companies based in the Far East that will carry out a quality audit for you before you release payment. Shipping times of around 14 weeks have also got to be factored in.

Custom Plastic Enclosure
Case study: Microwave Checker

This product measures radiation leakage from a microwave oven and was launched by Tele-Products around 7 years ago. The business plan projected sales of around 200 per annum and a sale price of £120. We had a budget of around £35 for the factory price for the Microwave Checker. (Factory price is the cost of materials and labour to manufacture the product and make it available for sale. It would normally include everything that is in the box when the product is sold.)

Injection moulding was not an option. A cost of around £10k for the tooling could not be justified. Amortising this over a 4 year expected product life would have put a price of £12.50 per unit cost on each product in addition to the cost of the parts. The cost of the mouldings would have been around £2 when set-up costs are taken into account. Additionally it was a speculative new product and we were not confident that sales of 200 per annum were achievable. An investment of £10k was considered to be too risky.

In the end, we opted for a semi-custom enclosure. The companies that provide this service work from a flat sheet of plastic and fold this to provide a custom enclosure. (See section on this technique at the end of this chapter).

The benefits of this approach are that you can have a case that is the size and shape that you want with all the right apertures machined in. Of course there are restrictions on the shape as there is a limit on how a flat sheet of plastic can be folded.

For the Microwave Checker, we ended up with three parts. A base and a top that clipped together with apertures for a switch, two LEDs and a bar graph display. There was also a battery compartment with a cover that was held on by a screw.

**The top, battery cover and the base
of the Microwave Checker**

There was a tooling cost of around £1k for this option and the three piece parts came to a total of £7 each when ordered in quantities of 250. Overall this was good solution as the design cost could be amortised to about a £1 over a 4 year life of the product. This gave us a cost of £8 for the enclosure ensuring that the overall product could be manufactured to budget.

PCB mounted inside the Microwave Checker

Notice how the entire assembly fits in the base with the lid just clipping on. This makes repair and calibration quite easy to carry out. There are no screws holding the 2 parts together. They just snap into place. For a product which has no dangerous voltages inside this is perfectly acceptable.

Set-up costs

With any job, there is usually a charge for starting it up. This is a fixed cost, irrespective of whether one is going to make 100 or 1000 units. The bigger the production run, the lower the set-up cost would be when amortised over the number being manufactured.

For example, say the actual cost of a moulding was £1 and the set-up cost was £200. If we were to manufacture 1000 units, the overall cost would be £1 plus 20p set-up cost per unit. However if the production run was only for 200 units, then the total cost would be £1 plus £1 for set-up costs.

Custom Metal Enclosure
Case study: PAT-IT Portable Appliance Tester

When this product was first planned in 2002, our expectation was to sell around 200 per annum. Hence we discounted an injection moulded case, for the same reasons as for the Microwave Checker. That is, we could not justify the cost of the tooling, as the product was speculative and we could not be sure whether we would recover the cost of our investment.

Instead we decided to go for a custom metal enclosure. The benefits of this approach was that there was no tooling costs, it gave us a robust enclosure with all the necessary apertures for displays and buttons and cost less than £10 when purchased in volumes of around 100.

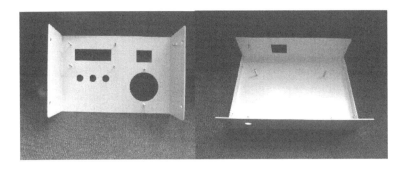

The top and the base of the PAT-IT enclosure

The case parts are powder coated to give them a nice finish. To complete the product, we used a custom label. The finished product can be seen below.

PAT-IT portable appliance tester

Although this approach gave us a good solution for the enclosure, the internal assembly gave us issues during maintenance. The top of the case held the switches, connectors and the display while the base held the main PCB assembly. When opening the case to gain access to the electronics, the length of the wire looms prevented an engineer from working on the PCB without disassembling the whole case.

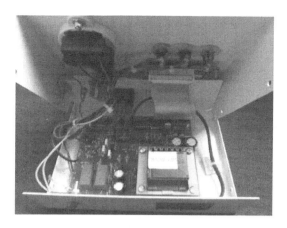

Inside the PAT-IT

One way this could have been overcome is to assemble the PCB into the lid of the PAT-IT with the base just being a covering. This would have made access to the electronics a lot easier.

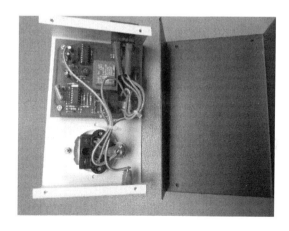

Product design with entire assembly in the lid

Design for disassembly

It is important to put some thought into what happens to the product after it has been sold. Many of the products that I have been involved with have been in use for more than 10 years. In this period, they are often returned for calibration or repair. A good design engineer will design in easy disassembly, to allow the repair technician quick access to the electronics.

End of life considerations are also important. Under the WEEE regulations (more on this later) electronic products are prevented from being dumped in landfill. When they have reached the end of their useful life, they are disassembled in recycling facilities and all useful components are recovered. A good engineer would keep this mind when designing enclosures and the way PCB assemblies fit inside them.

The BattPAT assembly just slides into the extrusion

Off-the-shelf Plastic Enclosure
Case study: Meteor

This was a product that we launched in 1997 and still sells in reasonable volumes. For this product we opted for a very simple enclosure. We bought an off-the-shelf plastic enclosure and machined it to take the PCB assembly. The plastic box costs us around a £1 and the machining costs another £1. The machined box and the way the PCB assembly fits inside this is shown below.

Meteor enclosure and PCB assembly

Back in 1997, if we had a crystal ball and knew that we were going to be still selling this product in 2012, we may well have opted for a injection moulded solution. But often when designing and launching a product one does not have this luxury. The design approach we chose for the Meteor was a low risk one and the cost of the enclosure was well within budget.

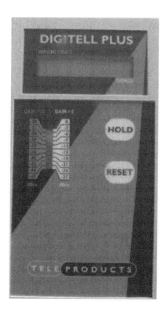

**Digitell dialled digit analyser used
a machined off-the-shelf enclosure**

There are many benefits in choosing an off-the-shelf plastic enclosure for products. There is very little up-front cost and products can be bought to market very fast. The disadvantage is that the products do not look unique. However this can usually be overcome by careful use of labels.

3D printing

This technology is now widely accessible with small 3D printers now available for less than £1000. This is great for printing one-off prototypes very quickly for evaluation and check out various designs.

For manufacture of cost effective enclosures for electronic products, this technology is not currently suitable, unless one is manufacturing very low volumes. However this situation might change over the next few years.

Summary

The choice of the right enclosure depends on a number of factors. The sales forecast for the product will drive this choice. For a product that is going to be made in large volumes, an injection moulding is probably the right way to go. If a company is launching a product speculatively and is not sure of volumes, then there are a number of other low risk approaches available.

The benefits of Bafbox - a plastic folding technology
Ian Watson
Sales Manager, Custom Design Technologies

In 1986 David Thompson and a French colleague started Bafbox which stood for British and French Box. This technique used CNCs, routers and saws to cut and groove plastic. Then heat was used to fold the boxes so that they can clip together.

Plastic sheet with groove, cut-outs
and circular holes for bosses

Enclosures are made using CAD software so designs can be changed at the click of a mouse. No special tooling is required. If speed to market is very important then the Bafbox technique is ideal. Typically we can design and manufacture a prototype within 5 days and production in some cases within 2 to 3 weeks.

We can also cope with frequent customer changes e.g. due to changes of the front screen, fixing points for PCBs or connectors changing due to changing technology. We can machine push out options so the customer may use the same basic box for more than one product and just push out the holes they need for each product.

Case study
Motorsport fire extinguisher controller

When one of motorsport's leading manufacturers of fire and safety systems needed a new enclosure for its on-vehicle fire extinguisher systems, the company turned to us. The result was a simple two-piece Bafbox plastic housing produced in ABS with a laminated coating to provide the carbon-fibre look so beloved of the motorsport industry.

Fire extinguisher controller in 2-part Bafbox

The plastic enclosure replaced a previous housing made from die-cast metal and offered a significant advantage in terms of weight, an important consideration in all motorsport applications. The Bafbox also offered savings on production costs as it was supplied pre-drilled and screen printed. The original die-cast metal box had to be drilled, sent out for powder coating and then have labels applied.

The overall effect of the new Bafbox enclosure was a more professional look as well as being far easier to assemble and makes the overall system easier to maintain.

The new on-vehicle fire extinguisher system has proved so popular that it now features on a number of leading racing cars in Formula 3 and Formula 3000.

Based in Oxfordshire and with more than 25 years experience of providing custom solutions for customers in the electronics industry, customDesignTechnologies encompasses Bafbox custom enclosures, customKeypads membrane switch panels and customAssembly for cost effective and flexible electronic and mechanical assembly services for companies looking to out-source manufacturing.

www.cdt123.com

Benefits of good industrial design - BattPAT tester
Peter Farrer
Design Consultant, Glenelg Product Design

In 2006, Glenelg were commissioned to carry out the industrial design for a new test instrument for First Stop Safety to replace the PAT-IT tester.

The existing product consisted of a costly fabricated box and overlay. Whilst fabrication is often the first route in the development of electronics enclosures, with little or no investment required, the unit cost of enclosure is often significantly higher than other manufacturing techniques. Fabrication often impacts on the speed of manufacture and assembly.

Whilst the PAT-IT was functionally comparable with competitor products its visual appearance lost it sales against the more aesthetic brand leaders.

The design brief presented to Glenelg proposed a significantly improved aesthetic keyed with reduced manufacturing costs and improved speed of assembly. The investment available allowed for some tooling but was short of that required for a fully injection moulded product.

The size of enclosure necessary for the BattPAT would have required injection mould tooling in excess of £20k. Annual projected sales around 1000 units meant the on cost of tooling investment even spread over 2 years would have added £10 to the unit cost, this on top of the moulded part cost and electronic elements.

Designing to a projected volume of 1000 units per year and a maximum investment of £10k Glenelg had at their disposal vacuum forming, pressure forming, plastic and aluminium extrusions and small scale injection mouldings.

Vacuum and pressure forming were discounted early in the process because of the high cost of finishing to provide a standard suitable for such a product.

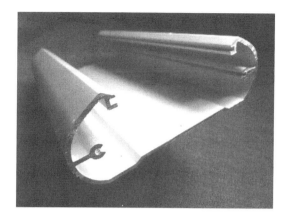

Aluminium extrusion with slots for electronic assembly

The environment and required durability led quickly to a final concept based around an aluminium extrusion. At a cost of £700 for die tooling, extrusions provided the ideal central body structure allowing for a fast linear assembly. Anodising was chosen over powder coating. Anodising provides an anti-chip, anti-scratch, high quality finish. The assembly consisting of the membrane keypads, metal plate and PCB simply slid into the extrusion.

A singular universal injection moulded end-cap seals both ends of the extrusion at a modest tooling cost of less than £10k. Moulded in 'rubber like' TPE (thermoplastic elastomer) the end-caps provide a tough yet soft impact resistant coloured contrast to the hard crisp silver extrusion.

Moulded end cap

Improved aesthetics and functions allowed the product to be sold through catalogues and other outlets etc that would not have considered the original fabricated product.

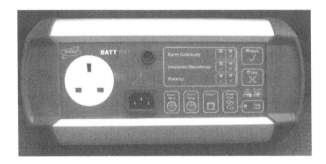

BattPAT tester

This project delivered an attractive product which was easier to make, at a reduced cost with minimal investment in tooling.

Glenelg are a design consultancy based in West Yorkshire, UK, who specialise in producing innovative product and packaging design solutions, taking ideas from concept to production

www.glenelgdesign.com

PCB Technology

When turning a product from a prototype into one that is ready for manufacture, it is important to have an understanding of the different PCB technologies available. Often the right choice is driven by the expected volume going through manufacture. An experienced manufacturing engineer will help the budding electronics engineer make the right choice. This chapter gives the newly graduated engineer an overview of the different technologies.

Through-hole Technology
Case study: Viscount telephone

For many years the use of through-hole components was the dominant technology for PCBs. Certainly, when I started off in the industry in 1979 and was involved in the mass produced Viscount telephones, all the components used in this were through-hole ones. Below is an image of the Viscount assembly using a range of through-hole components. A single sided PCB is used to reduce cost. As the name implies, the component legs went through holes in the PCB and were soldered on the other side of the board.

Viscount single sided PCB assembly

Our main concern with the design of the PCB for the Viscount telephone was to maximise the use of axial components. Automatic component insertion machines for axial components like resistors and diodes were far more common than those that were capable of handling radial components like transistors and capacitors. Many manufacturing departments had already invested in axial insertion machines.

In the end, the manufacturing line for the Viscount telephone utilised an axial, radial and IC insertion machines to meet the anticipated production volumes of 10,000 units a week.

In a high volume production line a flow soldering machine was the natural choice. Once the components were assembled in the PCB, the component legs were cropped and clenched to hold them in place and then the whole assembly was passed through the flow soldering machine.

Flow soldering machine

Mixed Technology
Case study: Meteor

When we were designing the Meteor back in 1997, Surface Mount technology was readily available. Here the components sit on the surface of the PCB on pads and are soldered in place. One benefit of using surface mounted components is that they are much smaller and one can condense complex designs into a tiny space.

PCB assembly with surface mounted components

Another advantage is that the same pick-and-place machine can handle resistors, diodes, capacitors, transistors and ICs. With through-hole components different types of machines are required for axial or radial components.

Component feeders for SMT pick and place machine

The anticipated volumes for the Meteor Plus were in the region of 50 a month. A few of the sub-contract manufacturers that we were planning to use did not have a pick and place machine in house. Also with such a small volume going through production, they could manufacture the board by using manual insertion of components and still be competitive with manufacturers that were using the latest pick and place machines. In addition, space on the PCB was not a problem.

Manual PCB assembly

As we did not need the 2 major benefits provided by SMT components, we took the decision to use through-hole technology for the first version of the Meteor. The finished board was hand soldered. This was an example of using appropriate technology and not the latest technology, as this gave us a wider choice of sub-contractors to use. A double sided PCB was used because of the density of the components.

Meteor PCB assembly with through hole components

However with the advent of the RoHS regulations (more on this later) one of the ICs that we were using proved difficult to replace. The only alternative available was a SMT component. This resulted in a redesign of the PCB with use of SMT and through-hole components. The manufacturing process for this was slightly different.

A silk screen was used to apply solder paste to the pads of the SMT components that were to be used. The SMT IC was placed by hand with the slightly "tacky" paste holding it in place. The board was then heated in an infrared oven causing the solder paste to "reflow" and solder the SMT components in place. Following this, the through-hole components were inserted and manually soldered as before.

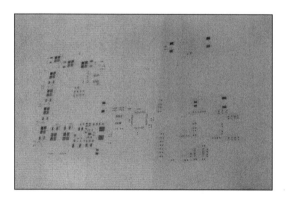

Silk screen for applying paste

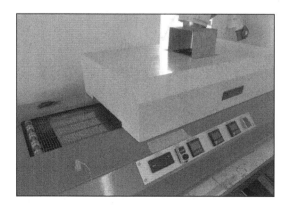

Infrared reflow oven

By designing the PCB to use the most appropriate technology, the Meteor has been economically manufactured over a number of years.

Surface Mount Technology
Case study: Comet

This product was designed and launched in 2011 as an updated Meteor with a USB port. Anticipated volumes were in the region of around 1500 per annum. Based on this we took a decision to make this a board which maximised the use of SMT components. There were some electromechanical components, such as sockets and transformers which were still through-hole.

Comet PCB assembly with mostly SMT components

On this PCB you can see that all the SMT components are on top side of the PCB only. The board initially has solder paste applied to the component pads, using a silk screen. All these components are placed by a pick and place machine and then the board is placed in the reflow oven. The through-hole components are then inserted by hand, and as there are only a few of these, they are hand soldered.

Surface Mount Technology
Case study: MemoryPAT

This product was launched early in 2012. It was designed from the start to use pick and place machine as it was a complex board with many components. Because of the high board density, there are SMT components on both sides of the PCB.

MemoryPAT PCB with SMD on both sides

The process for soldering the SMT components is similar to that described above except this time, solder paste is applied to both sides of the PCB. Then the SMT components are placed and the solder reflowed to fix the components in place. If the components on the 'under side' of the PCB are not too heavy, then the tackiness of the solder paste is enough to hold it in place during reflow. If the components are bigger, then there is a risk that they may fall off when the solder is reflowed. In this case, it is normal to apply glue to the middle of the body of the component to hold it firmly in place during the reflow process.

Flexible PCBs
Case study: BattPAT Membrane Keypad

The use of flexible PCBs is now well advanced. The most common application of this is in membrane keypads where LEDs and keypad buttons are soldered into a layer of a keypad. This was an approach that we adopted in the BattPAT battery powered tester.

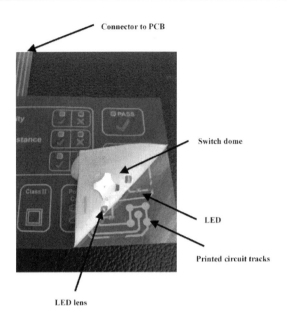

Connector to PCB

Switch dome

LED

Printed circuit tracks

LED lens

Membrane keypad construction

There are many benefits in using a membrane keypad. One of the key advantages is that the whole mechanical assembly is much simpler. If switches and LEDs are held on a rigid PCB just below the lid of the enclosure, then one has to pay a lot of attention to the mechanical fixing of the PCB at exactly the right height. There has to be the right apertures in the lid for the switches and LEDs and great attention paid to tolerances.

Digitell front panel assembly

For example in our Digitell Plus product, the assembly was quite tricky with even a 1mm shift causing the switches not to work.

Once the switches and LEDs are moved to a separate flexible PCB, then all this complexity disappears. All one needs is a slot on the lid of the enclosure for the ribbon cable to pass through.

Summary

The choice of the right PCB technology depends on a number of factors. The sales forecast for the product will drive this choice. For a product that is going to be made in large volumes, a fully SMT board is the best approach. This will help the use of automatic placement machines for increased speed and accuracy of manufacture.

If a smaller volume product is under consideration, then a mixed technology board is probably more appropriate as this will give us increased flexibility in the choice of manufacturer.

COMPLIANCE

Before an electronic product can be made available for sale, there are many requirements that it has to meet. These are often to do with product safety and are intended to protect the user and the environment. In this section we cover some of the most common requirements.

Electrical Safety

Electromagnetic Compatibility

Environmental Compliance

Declaration of Conformity

Electrical Safety

If your product is going to be powered by batteries or use an external plug top supply, then this subject is not a priority for you. However a well rounded electronics engineer should have an appreciation of electrical safety in a product. If your product is going to use mains voltage, then it is vital that you have a good understanding of this.

Low Voltage Directive

All electrical appliances supplied within the EU must comply with the Low Voltage Directive (LVD). This ensures that equipment provides a high level of protection to users. Any voltage greater than 30V AC or 60V DC is regarded as hazardous and users should be protected from direct contact with this without the use of a tool. A single fault should not result in users coming into contact with these voltages.

Class of construction

All electrical appliances using mains voltage have to provide at least 2 levels of protection to the user. This is to ensure that if one of the protection layers were to fail, there is the back-up of the second layer still in place. This makes electrical equipment very safe to use.

Depending on how exactly the protection is provided, electrical appliances are mainly of Class I or Class II construction.

Class I

Here the protection is provided by a combination of insulation and use of the mains Earth. It is best shown by referring to the photograph of an electric fire that has been taken apart.

Inside an electric fire

In the plug the three wires connect to the Live, Neutral and Earth pins. Inside the fire, the brown Live wire and the blue Neutral wire connect to a plastic connector. The green/yellow Earth wire connects to the metal case of the fire.

The user is protected from electric shock by the plastic insulation of the connector. This holds the Live and Neutral wires in place and prevents them from touching the metal case of this electric fire. This plastic insulation of the connector is known as basic insulation.

If this basic insulation were to fail, say due to excessive movement of the cable and the Live wire touches the metal case then the user of the fire can receive an electric shock if not for the fact that the Earth wire is present.

By connecting to the metal case of the electric fire, the Earth wire keeps all this metal at Earth potential. What this means is that it is impossible to get an electric shock even when the metal case of the fire is connected directly to the Live voltage. In practice a fuse would blow either in the plug or the main fuse box to protect the user.

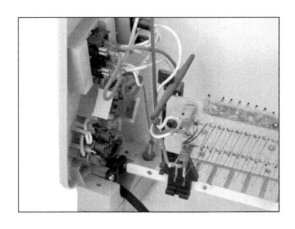

Close up of wiring inside the fire

In summary, in Class I appliances the user is protected by a combination of basic insulation and the provision of an Earth connection, thus providing two levels of protection.

Class II

In a Class II appliance, the user is protected by at least two layers of insulation. For this reason, Class II appliances are also known as 'double insulated'. They do not require an Earth connection.

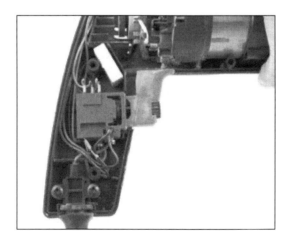

Inside an electric drill

This is a Class II electric drill which has been opened up. Inside one can see that as well as the plastic connector providing basic insulation, there is additional insulation provided by the plastic enclosure of the drill.

The user is therefore protected by two separate layers of insulation. Class II appliances are always indicated by the double box symbol on the rating plate.

Rating plate on drill with double box symbol

Levels of insulation

Engineers can use different levels of insulation to achieve the required safety in products that are powered by mains voltage. These are generally known as basic, supplementary and reinforced insulation. This is explained below.

Basic insulation

This is insulation that is used in conjunction with another method to protect the user from electric shock.

For example, in the electric fire we looked at earlier, the main protection was provided by the use of an earth connection. However the Live and Neutral wires are prevented from touching the metal case by the use of the plastic connector which provides basic insulation. Most Class I appliances use basic insulation along with the earth connection to provide 2 layers of protection.

Supplementary insulation

This is insulation that is provided in addition to basic insulation to protect the user. For example, in the drill we looked at earlier, the plastic enclosure can be considered to be providing supplementary insulation.

Reinforced insulation

When an insulating material is such that basic and supplementary insulation are provided together then this is known as reinforced insulation. If this insulation is provided by two separate layers, then this is known as double insulation. This is the type of insulation that is found in the drill we looked at earlier.

Creepage and Clearance

These refer to the safe spacing within products when you depend on air as an insulator. If you are designing a product that uses mains voltage then an understanding of this is very important.

Creepage

This is the spacing between live parts and low voltage parts along the surface of insulation. For example, when you have live tracks and low voltage tracks on a PCB, this is the safe spacing between the two.

The specification of what is acceptable depends on which level of insulation you are trying to achieve, the type of environment and many other factors and is too complex to go into here. As a rule of thumb, when I am having PCBs laid out and am trying to achieve reinforced insulation I allow 5 mm gap between live and low voltage tracks.

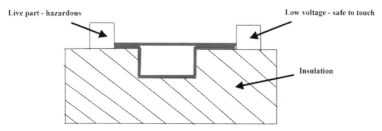

Green line - Clearance (distance through air)
Red line - Creepage (along the surface of the insulation

Live part - hazardous

Low voltage - safe to touch

Insulation

Difference between creepage and clearance

Clearance

This is the spacing through air between live parts and low voltage parts that the user can touch. For example, in the electric fire, this is the spacing between the heating element and the enclosure.

The specification of acceptable clearance distances again depends on a number of factors. In the electric fire where one is trying to achieve basic insulation, the required distance is 2mm.

Rating Plate

All electrical appliances must have a rating plate showing at least the following.

- Voltage of operation
- Power (or current consumption)
- Double Insulation mark if it is applicable
- Any special warnings (such as indoor use only)
- Appropriate approval markings (such as CE)
- Wheelie bin symbol to show users not to discard to landfill

Here are some examples of rating plates from a variety of appliances.

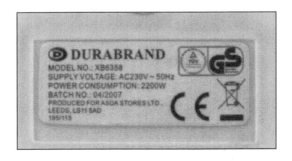

Selection of rating plates

Summary

Electrical safety is an important consideration for anyone involved in the design of equipment that uses mains voltage. This chapter introduces the engineer to some of the concepts. Further study and experience will be necessary before one can become competent in this field.

Electromagnetic Compatibility (EMC)

All electronics engineers involved in product development should have an appreciation of EMC. Many product designs have hit problems due to an inadequate understanding of this. The most recent example of this was the delay to the launch of the Raspberry Pi in 2012. The product launch was delayed for many months while all the required EMC testing was carried out.

EMC Directive

This European Union directive requires that products must not emit unwanted electromagnetic interference and must be immune to a normal level of interference. The majority of electrical products must comply with these requirements and compliance is usually shown by testing to harmonised standards.

The purpose of this directive is to make sure that electrical products from different sources can work alongside each other with little risk of mutual interference. Without this type of standard no manufacturer could guarantee that their products could work satisfactorily in the field.

There are harmonised standards that are applied throughout Europe to ensure that all manufacturers are working to the same requirements.

There are a number of product specific standards for assessing the EMC performance of equipment. For example there are standards for household appliances, lighting, IT equipment and fire alarms. Where a product standard does not exist there are generic standards that can be applied.

Emissions testing

This is carried out for radiated emissions by measuring field strength and conducted emissions along connecting cables. Radiated emissions are usually tested by using an appropriate antennae and a spectrum analyser. The equipment is powered and put in its normal state of operation while the spectrum analyser is used to sweep through the frequency domain.

Hewlett Packard Spectrum Analyser

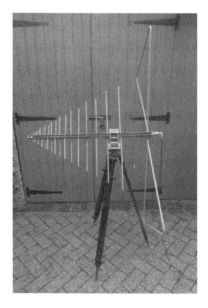

Antennae used for emissions measurement

The field strength of all the radiated signals from 30MHz up to 1000MHz is noted and compared with the limits in the standard for that type of equipment. Note that for some appliances assessment of radiation above 1000MHz is required.

When testing for unwanted radiated emissions, it is important to be aware of ambient RF signals. An experienced EMC test engineer will be alert to this and account for signals that are not originating from the unit being tested. For this reason, an RF shielded room is often used to carry out much of the EMC testing.

Conducted Emissions are carried out on power and telecom network cables that are connected to the electrical equipment. When measuring this on the mains input, a Line Impedance Stabilisation Network (LISN) is normally used to allow the equipment to function normally and provide a connection point with the right impedance for the spectrum analyser. It also blocks unwanted signals present on the mains network from affecting the measurement. This is used to assess the levels of the unwanted signals from 150kHz up to 30MHz.

Line Impedance Stabilisation Network

Immunity testing

This testing includes subjecting the product to radiated and conducted RF signals, fast transient bursts and electro static discharge.

Immunity to radiated RF signals is measured by using a RF

signal generator, an RF amplifier and antennae to inject a high RF field around the product and check that it still performs correctly. When testing products for residential, commercial or light industrial environments, frequencies from 80MHz to 1000MHz are used usually at a field strength of 3V/m.

When testing products intended for industrial environments, field strengths of 10V/m is used as well as testing up to 2.7GHz. In this chapter most examples are drawn from the requirements for residential or commercial use. Please refer to the standards referred to in Appendix 4 for the appropriate test requirements.

Immunity to conducted interference is checked over a frequency range from 150kHz to 80MHz and using a level of 3V rms. The signal is injected into all the cables that are connected to the equipment under test under normal operation. A Coupling - Decoupling network (CDN) is used to inject the test signal into the cable.

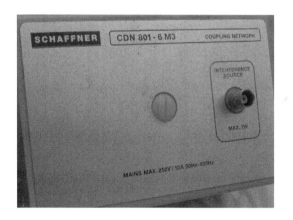

Coupling - Decoupling Network (CDN)

Testing with Fast Transient Bursts (FTB) is part of the immunity testing. FTBs are generated whenever appliances or circuits within them are switched on and off using mechanical switches. Manufacturers need to ensure that their equipment works as normal in the presence of these interference signals.

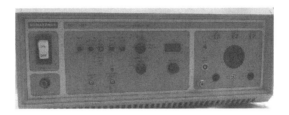

Fast Transient Burst generator

Bursts of pulses with a rise time of 5nS and duration of 50nS are capacitively coupled into mains and other cables while they are operating normally. Amplitudes of 0.5kV or 1kV are used depending on the type of port. The harmonised standards also specify the duration and repetition rate of the fast transient bursts.

The bursts of pulses are typically coupled into the cables of the unit under test using a capacitive clamp.

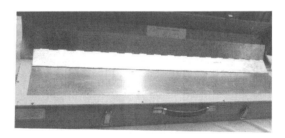

Capacitive clamp

Most people will have had the (unpleasant) experience of electrostatic discharge (ESD) to a metal object such as a filing cabinet or to a body of a car. The designer has to make sure that if this discharge was to a product they have designed or near it that it should continue to work normally. More importantly they need to ensure that there is no permanent damage as a result of a static discharge. For this reason testing for immunity to ESD is an important part of EMC testing.

An ESD gun is used for this testing with the product under test being placed on a large grounded metal sheet. Two types of discharges are used during this testing.

ESD gun with rounded and pointed tips

During contact discharge testing, a pointed tip is fitted to the ESD gun and testing is carried out up to a voltage of 4kV. The tip is bought into contact with the product while it is operating normally and the vacuum relay in the gun is triggered to deliver the current. This is repeated to different parts of the product, including connection ports and also to the metal plane on which the product is resting.

Air discharge testing is carried out up to 8kV using a rounded tip. After charging, the tip is brought close to the product until the voltage discharges across the air gap. This is repeated to different parts of the product being tested.

When carrying out ESD testing it is normal to start with relatively low voltages and slowly step up to the specified voltage. If adverse effects are noted early on, then fixes can be applied before restarting the tests. Most ESD guns allow testing to be carried out with both polarities of voltage.

Summary

Electromagnetic Compatibility is an important part of electronic product development. In my experience this subject is not taught well in most university engineering courses. EMC testing requires a lot of experience and is best left to those skilled in this area. However any engineer involved in electronic engineering should understand the requirements of this and take steps to give their products a good chance of passing these tests.

Designing for EMC - some tips
Martyn Gawthorpe
Managing Director, Continental Compliance Ltd

- EMC standards of performance are enforced through regulations, but first and foremost EMC performance should be considered as part of the general product specification for your product user. Supplement the ideas below using web searches, there's a wealth of good design guidance available.

- Consider EMC right at the very start of your development and apply basic design rules. By leaving it until later you will have lost useful opportunities for cost effective EMC performance improvement.

- Apply techniques in your PCB trace design that are known to provide good EMC performance. Use a ground (zero volt) trace network that offers good (low inductance) radio frequency connectivity across the PCB area.

- For circuits using very high frequency signals, for example microcontroller clock frequencies above a few 10s of MHz, a full ground plane on one layer is the ideal. Ground trace 'networks' can be built that improve grounding without a full plane by adding as many as possible 'redundant' extra ground traces between ground nodes in your circuit.

- Signal carrying traces are also a source of radio frequency coupling both to other parts of the circuit and directly in and out of your product. The physical loop area formed by these traces has a large impact on EMC performance. Where possible, keep PCB signal traces short. Place chips that are interconnected through signal traces physically close to one another on the PCB layout.

- Pay attention to the power supply decoupling capacitors associated with each active element of your circuit. The loop area of the traces formed by the capacitor placement is a source of radio frequency coupling as described above. The capacitor should be physically as close as possible to, for example a chip Vcc pin, with the grounded capacitor node returned to a 'good RF ground'.

- Place PCB interface connectors close to the circuit elements feeding them, not through lengthy traces.

- Carry out some basic EMC tests on your first prototype PCB. If you do not have access to EMC instruments a very useful first pass indicator is a domestic broadcast radio receiver, preferably with LW, MW, SW and FM bands. With the receiver around 1m away from your product, tune over all the bands listening for signals, turning your product on and off to confirm the origin. Listen to the strength of signals from other products around you and compare.

Martyn has worked in the field of Radio Frequency design and EMC compliance for more than 30 years. Having worked for many organisations as a design engineer, he founded RF Design in 1989 and Continental Compliance in 1992. All the images in this chapter have been supplied courtesy of Martyn.

Continental Compliance designs, manufactures and supplies instruments for amateur band, radio astronomy, tutorial and industrial applications.

www.rfdesignuk.com

Environmental Compliance

Many electronic consumer products, such as mobile phones, PCs and MP3 players are replaced regularly. The used items are then discarded as they have very little second hand value. This throw away culture has many implications to the environment if these products ends up in landfill sites. A number of environmental legislation has been put in place to manage this problem.

Waste Electrical and Electronic Equipment (WEEE) Regulations

The objective of the WEEE regulation is to prevent electronic equipment from ending up on landfill sites and to ensure that products are recycled or as much material as possible is recovered from the product.

WEEE man, made entirely of discarded electrical items stands some 7 m tall at the Eden project in Cornwall

The Regulations require any producer of Electrical and Electronic Equipment (EEE) in the EU to finance the costs of collection and treatment of waste products, in proportion to the amount by weight they place on the market. The term "producer" does not just refer to a manufacturer. It also refers to companies importing products into the EU.

The rating plate of all electrical and electronic products must carry the wheelie bin symbol to indicate to the user that these must not be discarded into "black bags" and landfill sites.

Wheelie bin symbol

Producers must register with an approved compliance scheme which will monitor the amount of product placed on the market and manage the safe disposal of the waste through an authorised recycling company. The registration fee and disposal costs are dependent on the weight of product placed on the market each year.

All products that need electricity to provide their primary function are covered by the WEEE regulations even if they are battery powered or need winding up. Components are exempt.

Restriction of Hazardous Substances (RoHS)

This EU directive places restriction on the use of hazardous materials in the manufacture of electrical and electronic products. Alongside the WEEE directive, it is aimed at tackling the problem of toxic waste ending up in landfill sites.

Some engineers refer to the RoHS directive as the lead free directive. In actual fact RoHS covers 6 substances as shown below.

- Lead (Pb)
- Mercury (Hg)
- Cadmium (Cd)
- Hexavalent chromium (Cr^{6+})
- Polybrominated biphenyls (PBB)
- Polybrominated diphenyl ether (PBDE)

The maximum permitted level is 0.01% for cadmium and 0.1% for the other 5 substances. These limits are by weight for each homogenous material used in the product and not as a percentage of the whole product. For example, there is a plastic component that weighs 10gms in a product that has a total weight of 2000gms. In this plastic component there is 0.05gms of PBDE which represents 0.5% by weight for the component and 0.0025% by weight for the product. In this example, the use of this plastic component would still be restricted in this product as it exceeds the 0.1% limit.

Lead is used widely in electronic components and for soldering. Mercury is used widely in some lighting products. Cadmium is used in plastic pigmentation and photo cells. Chromium is used in metal finishes. PBB and PBDE is used as flame retardants in several plastics. None of these are toxic in the traditional sense where direct exposure can cause death or severe injury. However studies over many years have shown that there can be adverse effects to health due to long term low levels of exposure to these materials.

The RoHs directive ensures that if large amounts of electronic wastes does end up in landfill sites, then the level of these toxic substances is kept to a low level. However with the

WEEE directive in place much of this waste would end up in recycling and recovery plants. The RoHS directive protects the health of the staff working in these facilities.

When this directive came into force in 2006, there was no symbol to indicate compliance. Some companies have adopted the symbol below to show that the product complies with the directive.

Example of a RoHS compliance symbol

The updated RoHS2 directive which came into force in 2013 required RoHS compliance to be included in the Declaration of Conformity (DOC) and covered by the CE mark.

CE mark

Summary

The WEEE and RoHS directives are intended to tackle the huge problem of toxic high tech waste. The WEEE directive compels manufacturers and importers to recycle products and recover more material at end of life. The RoHS directive protects workers in these industries as well the population at large from exposure to chemicals which can have long term toxic effect on their health.

Design for Recycling
Alan Dukinfield
Director, S2S Electronics Ltd

Electrical recycling companies have, for a long time, been considered as nothing more than scrap yards and indeed 20 years ago, many of the companies who started looking at Electrical and Electronic Equipment (EEE) recycling were metal recyclers looking to diversify. However, nowadays EEE recyclers have evolved into specialist companies offering a range of services not limited to metal reclamation.

Refurbishment and repair services are now commonplace. Component reclamation is now more common and redundant electrical equipment is now quite correctly considered as an asset as opposed to scrap.

Legislation has come into force over recent years and this has changed the focus away from disposal towards recycling and has certainly helped change the perception of scrap and assets. This includes the Landfill directive, the Hazardous Waste directive, and a raft of producer responsibility directives including the Batteries directive, the ErP directive and the WEEE directive.

As soon as the perception changes from scrap to an asset, manufacturers can start to look at the assets and how they can improve it at all levels of the lifecycle from design through to end of life.

The WEEE directive came into force a number of years ago and this has certainly been a driver for manufacturers to focus on the end of life management. Many EEE recycling companies offer a range of services around the WEEE directive. The services are not just limited to collection and processing of redundant product. Who better to offer advice on how the product comes apart than a recycler?

This logical development can be taken further with recyclers being able to get involved at the design stage to look at how the product is designed, the choice of materials and how it goes together to maximise the efficiency of recycling and minimise any costs. This 'sustainable design' approach has been used by S2S for a number of years and working in conjunctions with 'eco design' consultants, S2S have been able to offer practical advice at the design stage that has both improved design and saved costs for the producer.

An example of this can be seen with a product manufactured by S2S called a soft start. This product uses Thyristor technology to slowly start AC motors and avoid both mechanical and electrical stresses seen with conventional motor starting methods such as 'Direct on Line' or' Star/Delta' motor starting. Working with an experienced 'eco design' consultant, S2S looked at the product and the materials used and came up with a number of improvements which saved the business £30,000 per year, reduced the carbon footprint of the product and improved the end of life recycling performance of the product.

Simple changes that were made included:

- Using re programmable processor instead of 'one time' programmable processors on the main circuit board.
- Using recycled aluminium for the cooling heatsink as opposed to virgin aluminium.
- Optimising heatsink design to use smaller heatsinks to reduce the frame size of the product and reduce material content overall.
- Replacing the plastic end plates with aluminium end plates to ensure commonality of materials for end of life management.

Alan is an electrical engineer by trade having worked with an electronic/electrical contract manufacturer for 20 years. A founder and director of RID UK Ltd, he has been working on meeting the WEEE directive for a number of years helping companies find practical solutions to compliance and treatment issues.

RID UK is now part of the larger S2S Electronics Ltd, turning over £3M in contract electronics manufacturing and recycling. Alan is a director and shareholder in the business. He is currently involved in a number of projects looking at issues such as recovery of precious metals and the WEEE return system in conjunction with large UK consultants.

www.s2s.uk.com

Declaration of Conformity (DOC)

All electrical and electronic products sold in the European Economic Area (EEA) needs to comply with a number of harmonised requirements. This is to ensure that goods manufactured in one country can be freely marketed throughout this region without needing to be modified to meet separate requirements.

In the chapters above we have looked at electrical safety and electromagnetic compatibility requirements as well as environmental requirements such as WEEE and RoHS. If a product is for connection to the telephone line, then the requirements of the RTTE directive have to be met.

DECLARATION OF CONFORMITY

Tele-Products Ltd declares under our sole responsibility that the product listed below conforms to the CE marking Directive 768/2008/EC by complying with the EC Directives listed below.

Product: MemoryPAT – Battery Powered Portable Appliance Tester with Display and Memory

The assessment of conformity has been made using the following generic standards.

EMC Directive 2004/108/EC

EN 55022:2010 Class B   Conducted and Radiated Emissions

EN 61000-6-2: 2005   Immunity for Industrial Environments

Low Voltage Directive 2006/95/EC

BS EN 61010-1:2001   Safety requirements for electrical equipment for measurement, control, and laboratory use Part 1: General requirements.

RoHS Directive 2011/65/EU

We comply with this directive by quality control and audit of our suppliers and sub-contractors.

Signed: T. Segaran

Position: Technical Director

Date: 12th February 2013

Tele-Products Ltd
11, Glaisdale Road
Northminster Business Park
York
YO26 6QT

Note: Tele-Products Ltd trades as First Stop Safety when marketing the MemoryPAT.

Example of a Declaration of Conformity (DOC)

In most cases the manufacturer can declare compliance with the directives by carrying out testing and/or assessments of their products. Once they are satisfied that the requirements of the directives have been met, then they would need to produce a Declaration of Conformity (DOC) to state that the product complies with the harmonised standards that were used for this assessment.

Summary

Before a product can be made available for sale, there are a number of safety and inter-operability tests that have to be carried out. In many cases there are EU directives to cover this. It is up to the manufacturers to satisfy themselves that these have been met and make a declaration to this effect by issuing a Declaration of Conformity.

PROJECT MANAGEMENT

Good project management skills are essential in taking an electronic product from the prototype stage right up to where it is mass produced and available for sale. This section covers various aspects of this.

Project control

Production documentation

Pricing

Project Control

Graduate electronic engineers will soon find themselves in charge of projects. In managing these projects its important to adopt a methodology that delivers a well designed product that meets the requirements, is easy to manufacture at an acceptable cost and complies with the various EU directives. Here we look at some important aspects of project control.

Project plan

The primary responsibility of the project manager is to make sure that the product is delivered on time, perform as expected and meet the cost targets. A project plan outlining the key milestones is a good way of keeping a project on track. The major steps in the development of a typical electronic product are outlined below.

- Produce a functional specification from the marketing brief
- Build a working prototype, usually with a prototyping board
- Build an alpha sample, usually with a PCB
- Build a beta sample
- Prepare user documentation and final packaging
- Carry out a pre-production run
- Prepare for main production

DisplayPAT project plan		22nd Feb 2011											
February		March				April					May		
Week 8	Week 9	Week 10	Week 11	Week 12	Week 13	Week 14	Week 15	Week 16	Week 17	Week 18	Week 19	Week 20	Week 21
ALPHA SAMPLES		2 alpha samples complete d by Nick	Joint testing by Seggy and Nick	Apha samples fully compliant with product specification.									
BETA SAMPLES Drawings and 3-d modelling for metal work, membrane and end caps from Peter.	Seggy to order membrane, metal work and end caps for 10 beta samples.			PCB design for BETA samples completed by Arrow.	BOM for BETA samples completed by Arrow.	Quote from Arrow for 10 Beta samples. TP to order 10 Beta samples.					10 Beta samples complete d by Arrow.		

Typical project plan covering alpha and beta stages

In the steps above, I have assumed that an enclosure is already available for the product. If an injection moulded enclosure is required then the following stages will need to be added to the project plan.

- Industrial design
- Fabricated sample
- Tool design
- Sample moulded parts for the alpha or beta samples
- Tool modification if required
- Moulded parts for pre-production and main production

The project plan can easily be kept on a spreadsheet and monitored regularly. Complex projects are sometimes managed using Gantt or PERT charts. However, in my experience this is rarely required when managing the design of new electronic products.

Functional specification

This document is usually derived from the marketing brief which outlines the features and target selling price of the product. The functional specification is a document that should cover the detailed operation of the product, target manufacturing costs and all other information to allow any electronic engineer to carry out the design.

Below is a list of the type of some of the information that should be included in this document.

List of features - This should include the ones from the marketing brief as well as other features that can be added easily to enhance the appeal of the product.

Target manufacturing cost - This would depend on the margins that normally operate in this industry. For industrial products, this would normally be a third of the target selling price. For example if the product was going to sell for £450 then the manufacturing cost (parts and labour) should be less than £150.

Power source - Is the product going to be powered from a battery or mains. If from a battery then are we going to use a rechargeable battery or dry cells? What is the expected battery life? Is there going to be provision of a battery low indicator? These should be all outlined in the functional specification.

If the product is going to be mains powered then one will need to address the question of whether it's for sale just in the EU or destined for export outside this region. Should we use a switching power supply with an input range from 100 to 240V to allow us to adopt the product easily for different mains voltages?

PSU with wide input voltage range

User controls - The functional specification should outline all the user controls such as buttons and switches. There should be a brief outline of the intended use of these controls.

User outputs - Most products use LCDs or LEDs to indicate information to the user. These should be included in this document along with the type of information they convey to the user.

Listed above is just some of the information that should be included in a functional specification. The objective of this document is that it can be passed to any design team to allow it to get on with the task of designing an electronic product.

User guide

In most projects, the user guide is written at the end of the project. In my experience of designing electronic products, writing this at the beginning of the project can be very useful. Although the functional specification outlines all aspects of the product, it is from the point of view of a designer. The user guide on the other hand is from the point of view of a user and writing this can often produce some valuable information for inclusion in the functional specification.

Design test specification

In the chapter on testing we emphasised the importance of design verification testing. This is a key element of good project management. At every major milestone the product must be checked against the design test specification to see if it is meeting the requirements of the functional specification. In fact the design test specification is largely derived from the functional specification with detail on how to carry out the tests.

The detail in this document must be such that it can be passed to an engineer who will then be able to carry out all the required testing.

Snagging list

This is in effect a list of all the non conformances found during the design testing. During the various stages of the project the person in charge will need to keep a list of these and notes on how they were resolved. They can then be discussed at the design reviews.

I have found it useful to keep the snagging list in the "cloud" so that personnel from different sites can have input into this important document.

Design reviews

These reviews are a good way of making sure that knowledge and experience from the different departments in the company are used in the design of new products. These should be run by a senior technical person in the company with input from marketing, manufacturing, service and technical support personnel. In my experience, projects that are managed this way result in good market leading products.

Design reviews are ideally carried out at the following stages of a project.

- When a functional specification has been prepared
- Once a working prototype is available.
- After an alpha sample has been through the design verification testing
- Once a beta sample has been through the design verification testing
- Following the pre-production run.

Summary

Electronic design engineers will soon find themselves either as a member of a development team or managing projects. This chapter is an introduction to good practice in this area. A good project plan taking in the different elements outlined above will ensure that a product can be delivered on time, perform as expected and meet the cost targets.

Production documentation

Preparing a product for manufacture either within the company or using a sub-contractor is an important aspect of designing and launching electronic equipment. Errors in production documentation can be costly to rectify and cause delays to product launches.

This chapter highlights some of the documents that are required to allow the product to be manufactured in volume by a third party.

Bill of Materials

This document is essential for defining any electronic product. For example, the Bill of Materials (BOM) for the printed circuit board assembly would list every item that is fitted to the board. It would list a unique definition for the part, the circuit position, where to buy it from and any special fitting instructions.

An ideal BOM would also list alternative sources for a part. This is useful when a part is hard to find or when trying to get a good price from a supplier. Single sourced parts can be a problem if the supplier stops manufacturing the item.

Bill of Materials (BOM) for a PCB assembly

Where it comes to custom designs such as the PCB or

programmable devices the BOM should refer to a separate specification for these items.

Assembly drawings

The BOM is a list of items and is primarily aimed at the person sourcing the parts. It does not show how the product goes together. This is the objective of the assembly drawings. This document should show where the components go on the PCB, their orientation and any special fitting instructions. Along with the BOM they should allow any electronics manufacturing company to build the product.

When the BOM and the assembly drawings are passed to a manufacturing facility, the production engineer responsible would normally use these to produce detailed work instructions. These are used by the production staff as a step by step instruction to build the product. However these documents are not easily transferrable from one facility to another as many of these instructions are company specific.

Final Assembly

Electronic product assembly usually consists of two stages. There is the manufacture of the PCB assembly, which is largely an automated process and then the assembly of this into an enclosure which can be mainly a manual procedure.

This assembly stage usually has its own bill of materials and assembly drawings to ensure that the finished product can be mass produced correctly.

Production test specification

We covered the requirement for this in an earlier chapter. The production test is for checking that the design has been manufactured as planned.

It is important to avoid the tendency to over test at the production stage. The objective at this stage is to determine that the design has been manufactured correctly - i.e. the right components have been inserted (or placed) and soldered correctly. The production test is NOT intended to be a design verification test.

An experienced design engineer should be able to get the right level of testing to ensure the manufacture of a working quality product.

Change control

Once a product is in manufacture there is sometimes a need to change the design. This could be addressing some problem, to replace a hard to source component, to improve the design or reduce the manufacturing cost. This could be a change to the hardware or to the firmware in the product. It is very important to manage this change properly.

Many companies have a change control procedure in place to manage this. The engineer proposing the change usually completes an Engineering Change Note (ECN) which outlines the details of the change. Once this has been signed off, the production documentation is updated and the issue changed.

For example, for a document that is at issue state 1.0 the issue is changed to 1.1 for a minor change or issue 2 for a major change. Definitions differ between companies, but we tend to adopt a system where a change which only impacts one document is a minor change while one that may need a change to the user manual will be considered a major change.

ENGINEERING CHANGE NOTE 101

DATE: **25ᵗʰ August 2011**

PRODUCT: A/NZ BattPAT

FROM SERIAL / VERSION NUMBER: A/NZ1133106 / **TBA (internal TP use)**

REASON FOR CHANGE: Improve Earth Continuity measurement accuracy

CHANGES: Please see above reasons for changes in brackets

IMPLEMENTATION OF CHANGE:

SELECT	OPTION
x	Immediate
	On next production batch
	When current parts run out
	Other

DOCUMENTS AFFECTED:

DOCUMENT	CHANGE	BEFORE CHANGE	AFTER CHANGE
Parts List	x		
Circuit Diagram			
Test Specification			
Manual			
Data Sheet			
Calibration Form			
Source Code	x	1.8	2.0
Software disc			
Website			

ANY OTHER COMMENTS: Change must only be applied to units from Serial Number *A/NZ1133106*

RAISED BY: Seggy   APPROVED: **Seggy**

CIRCULATE TO:

SELECT	PERSON
X	MD (always)
	FSS Sales
	CT Sales
x	TP Ops
	FSS Cals
	Accounts
x	Sub-contractor (specify)

Example of an engineering change note (ECN)

When changing firmware within a microcontroller, the checksum can be used to keep track of different revisions. In products with embedded software, allowing the casual user to check the revision status of the firmware is a good idea. This will allow technical support staff to check the revision status over the telephone and decide if a product needs to come back for upgrade.

When evaluating changes it is up to the engineer to decide what level of testing needs to be carried out to check for any unforeseen side effects of the change. With firmware, it is not unusual to create a new problem when fixing bugs. It is a good idea to put the product through either the whole or part of the design verification test before any change is implemented in production.

Summary

Many engineers new to the field of product design may assume that once they have a working prototype, their task is complete. Nothing could be further from the truth. Getting a product ready for manufacture is an essential part of a design engineer's role within a company. This chapter goes through some of the documentation that is required to allow any manufacturing facility to successfully mass produce the item.

Pricing

After some thought I have introduced this chapter here, as designing a product to a target cost is an essential part of good engineering. During the last 35 years I have seen much of electronic manufacturing move to the Far East. If we can train a new generation of engineers to design competitively priced products then there is no reason why we cannot carry on manufacturing electronic products in the EU.

Factory costs

When costing products, it is important to come to an overall figure that includes everything that goes into the manufacture. This includes the cost of the materials and labour costs in manufacturing and testing the product. It's normal to exclude research and development, tooling and other one off costs that do not go directly into the cost of manufacturing. When adding up the figures, items such as the cardboard box used to package the product, plastic bags, fixing screws, power supplies, cables and batteries have to be included to come up with a total figure.

The volumes in which a product is manufactured will have a large impact on this cost. For example, on one of the products that I have been involved in, manufacturing the product in volumes of 500 off instead of 100 off results in price reduction of more than 20%.

Scheduling deliveries is a good way of benefiting from larger volumes. For example, if the forecast for a product is 500 over a period of a year, then many sub-contractors will accept an order for 500 and schedule deliveries of this product at a rate of 100 every 2 months.

The benefit to the sub-contract manufacturer is that they have a guaranteed order book for the product for the next 12 months. The design and the manufacturing company benefits by buying parts in higher volumes. The design company only has to pay for the product after each delivery is made and there is no impact on cash flow.

Scheduling on this scale only works when manufacturer and customer are geographically close and shipping costs are minimal. Most Far Eastern manufacturers work on high volumes which have to be paid for in advance. With high shipping costs they cannot usually provide this type of benefit to design companies.

Profit

Profit expectations are very different for different types of organisations. Traditional engineering companies normally do not sell directly to the end user. They tend to sell through a distribution network. For example, companies making lighting products use electrical wholesalers to reach their end customers. In this case, a product costing £70 and a list price of £200 would be sold to a wholesaler for around £ 130 to £150. The cost of sale would be borne by the wholesaler and the manufacturer would make a profit of around £70 per item.

Some engineering companies tend to establish a direct sales network to reach their end customers. The cost of advertising, stock, providing sales advice and technical support to the customer would all have to be paid for out of the profits made.

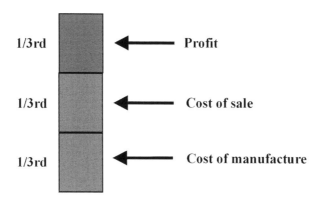

Breakdown of sale price

A good rule of thumb to adopt is a third for manufacture, a third for cost of sales and a third profit. The profit is to be used to pay for the research and development and any tooling, as well create a fund for the development of new products.

Summary

Profit is good. It pays for the cost of designing the product and provides funds for the design of new products. The design engineer's task is to get the factory costs down to a level where the product generates good profits for the company.

APPENDIX 1

Managing quality - ISO9001

Many electronic engineers graduate without ever hearing the term "quality control" or ISO9001. However, someone involved in designing and manufacturing electronic products needs to have a good working knowledge of this subject.

Quality management systems

Most companies have some sort of system to ensure that they provide products and services that are needed by their customers while complying with legal requirements and producing a profit for their shareholders. If they did not do this they would not survive for long in a competitive environment. Many organisations do this in an ad-hoc fashion and do not document the decision making process.

When the systems for doing this are documented they are known as a Quality Management System. ISO9001 is a published standard that provides a framework for companies to follow.

Once an organisation has a documented quality management system in place then it can seek ISO9001 certification. This can often provide an advantage over competitors that do not have this formal certification. Some customers may insist on ISO9001 certification from their suppliers.

One of the requirements of ISO 9001 can be summarised as follows.

"When developing new products, the business plans the stages of development, with appropriate testing at each stage. It tests and documents whether the product meets design requirements, regulatory requirements, and user needs."

In the chapters on Project control and Production

documentation, we covered the need for a project plan, design reviews, proper documentation and change control. All these elements help organisation manage projects effectively.

Organisations that adopt these processes will find it much simpler to achieve ISO9001 certification.

ISO 9001 and its benefits to businesses
Ray McDonough
Operations Director of Anode Electronics

There are many standards in the ISO range; ISO 9001:2008 gives the criteria for a quality management system. It is not restricted to manufacturing and is widely used by many organisations large and small.

The standard is based on key quality management principles involving top management and a structured approach to business processes. Continual improvement is a key part of the standard and is demonstrated through audits of the system and corrective actions. There are many publications that can guide you through how to write a quality manual and the certification process but it is important to remember that it must be an accurate reflection of your key processes. One method is the use of flow charts which will give a visual representation of the organisational systems and areas where improvements can be made.

Having mapped out the process, areas of training will be identified. These should be recorded on a skills matrix which is a simple spreadsheet showing what skills are required to perform the task against the skills of the people involved. Having identified any shortfall a training plan can be put together.

When writing your procedures, consider that these are job performance aids and not specific work instructions. They should give an overview of the process including any key measures and how and when functions must be performed. Should you require more detailed information such as how to operate key machinery then these are written as separate documents and referenced in the procedures. The same applies to drawings, bills of materials and other technical documentation.

Audits are a key process to check that the quality management system is working. This may involve an outside agency for annual certification. The auditor will gather evidence against what has been written as proof that the procedures are being followed. Any discrepancies will be discussed with the process owner and a corrective action plan put in place. This is all part of demonstrating continual improvement.

Another method is identifying, recording and monitoring of key business measures; if you can't measure it you can't manage it so choose carefully which ones are key to your business.

We all handle documentation every day from forms that are filled out, instructions to follow to drawing specifications. It is essential that these documents are error free and controlled. You cannot build a product using out of date drawings or budget a business with an incorrect financial statement. The standard requires the control of these documents however the degree of control will depend on the importance of the document. Any business related document must be controlled. However the quality policy could be signed by all directors whilst a work instruction can be signed by the process manager.

How these documents are controlled either on paper or electronically is dependent on the business but the use of revision levels and a good change control system is necessary.

It is important to understand the reasons why you have this standard. It demonstrates to your customers that you have a sound management system and will ensure they receive consistent good quality goods. This will in itself bring additional business benefits. The standard requires the involvement of top management and their commitment to its principles. This will be demonstrated by defining the companies' policies and ensuring the availability of the resources needed to perform them.

Having spent 14 years in the RAF, Ray joined GSPK where he was a Project Manager. He has accumulated a vast experience of the electronics manufacturing industry while working at GSPK and BVM. He is currently Operation Director at Anode Electronics, an electronics sub-contract manufacturer based in Knaresborough in North Yorkshire.

www.anodeelectronics.co.uk

APPENDIX 2

Prototyping circuits

Many projects that I have worked on have taken a similar path from idea to finished product. The stages in this process have been as follows.

- Working prototype
- Alpha sample
- Beta sample
- End products

When preparing a working prototype, my preference is to use a Vero board. This allows me to fully test the circuit out before committing to a PCB.

Working prototype on Vero board

Of course, when working with SMT devices this is not often easy to do. However there are adaptor boards that allow designers to fix SMT integrated circuits onto a Vero board for prototyping purposes.

If there are too many SMT components to make this viable, then another approach for the working prototype is to lay out a very large PCB with plenty of prototyping area. This will allow the engineer plenty of scope to carry out modifications while working on the first prototype.

Once the designer is happy with the working prototype, then the first version of the PCB can be laid out. The outline of this will be as required to fit in the enclosure.

Once the PCB is designed, the file format that is produced is known as the Gerber files. These are sent to a board manufacturer for the first sample PCBs. When built up, this will become the Alpha samples with a high confidence of working.

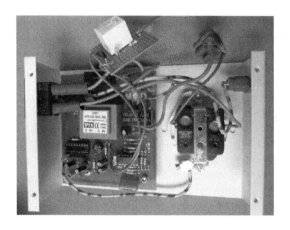

Alpha sample with various modifications

If the Alpha sample has very few modifications and fits in the enclosure properly, then preliminary EMC tests can be carried out on these. However if there are too many fixes or they do not fit in the case due to errors then it is safest to leave the EMC testing to the Beta sample stage.

On most projects, by the time the Beta samples are prepared, many of the problems have been ironed out and there is a high level of confidence in the performance of the product. Often the Beta samples can be used for field trial and shown to potential customers.

If further minor modifications are necessary following EMC tests, field trials or issues that are raised in design reviews, then these can be carried out prior to moving to production.

APPENDIX 3

Pareto Analysis

This is a useful technique to adopt when carrying out fault analysis on production failures or field returns. This is based on the Pareto principle that a disproportionately large percentage of errors or defects in any process are usually caused by relatively few problems.

Sometimes this principle is also known as the 80/20 rule and can be applied to many different types of analysis. In the 19th century, Vilfredo Pareto showed that income was distributed unevenly, with about 80% of the wealth in the hands of about 20% of the people. He was an Italian economist and this technique is named after him.

When applied to failure analysis, one will usually find that the majority of the faults are due to a few causes. Pareto analysis will help identify these few causes and once these are eliminated, there will be a significant drop in failures.

The technique is quite simple to apply. Once you have a list of reasons for the failures, simply write them down in decreasing order of frequency. Below is a sample list following the analysis of 20 failed boards.

Failure of TR1	7
Poorly soldered joint on C2	5
D1 the wrong way round	3
RL1 faulty	1
Solder bridge on XT1	1
R14 missing	1
C14 wrong value	1
Poor soldered joint on TR2	1

Start by tackling the ones at the top of the list and solve this. Find the cause for TR1 failing and implement a solution for this. Then work through the next two. Once these solutions have been implemented there should be a significant decrease in the number of failures because you have fixed 75% of the failures by concentrating on just three items.

Adopting the Pareto technique allows an engineer to focus on the most important issues and make effective use of their time.

APPENDIX 4

Harmonised standards

In the section on Compliance there was mention of various standards that are available for checking for compliance. Below is a list of the more commonly used standards.

RF Emission

EN61000-6-3	Generic emission standard: Residential, commercial and light industrial environments.
EN61000-6-4	Generic emission standard: industrial environment
EN55011	Industrial, scientific and medical (ISM) radio-frequency equipment – Electromagnetic disturbance characteristics – Limits and methods of measurement
EN55014-1	Electromagnetic compatibility - Requirements for household appliances, electric tools and similar apparatus - Emission
EN55022	Information technology equipment - Radio disturbance characteristics - Limits and methods on measurement

RF Immunity

EN61000-6-1	Generic immunity standard, Part 1: residential, commercial and light industry environment

EN61000-6-2	Generic immunity standard, Part 2: industrial environment

Electrical Safety

EN60950-1	Information technology equipment - Safety - General requirements
EN61010-1	Safety requirements for electrical equipment for measurement, control, and laboratory use - General requirements
EN60335-1	Household and similar electrical appliances - Safety - General requirements
EN60065	Audio, video and similar electronic apparatus - Safety requirements
EN50144-1	Safety of hand-held electric motor operated tools - General requirements

APPENDIX 5

Further reading

In my experience, although the internet is a useful tool for checking for snippets of information, it is hardly the right format for giving you the whole picture or a good grounding in a subject. There is nothing like a good book written by someone with wide experience in a subject. Below is a list of books that I have found useful in my career.

Electrical Product Safety
A step-by-step guide to LVD self assessment
Jimmy Tzimenakis & Dave Holland

EMC for Product Designers
Tim Williams

The Business of Electronic Product Development
Fabian Monds

Making It
Chris Lefteri

Achieve Total Quality
David Hutchins

17146473R00073

Printed in Great Britain
by Amazon